DEATHLOK THE DEMOLISHER

D1634888

RIC

MARVEL POCKET BOOK — Deathlok The Demolisher: Origins

Deathlok The Demolisher: Origins, Marvel Pocketbook Vol. 1. Contains material originally published in magazine form as Astonishing Tales #25-28 & 30-35. Published by Panini Publishing, a division of Panini UK Limited. Mike Riddell, Managing Director. Alan O'Keefe, Managing Editor. Mark Irvine, Production Manager. Marco M. Lupoi, Publishing Director Europe. Ed Hammond, Editor. Samuel Taylor, Assistant Editor. Angela Hart, Designer. Office of publication: Brockbourne House, 77 Mount Ephraim, Tunbridge Wells, Kent TN4 8BS. Licensed by Marvel Characters B.V. www.marvel.com. All rights reserved. No similarity between any of the names, characters, persons and/or institutions in this edition with those of any living or dead person or institution is intended, and any such similarity which may exist is purely coincidental.

Printed in the UK.

ISBN: 978-1-84653-194-1

MARVEL
marvel.com
© 2014 MARVEL

MIX
Paper from
responsible sources
FSC® C002386

DEATHLOK THE DEMOLISHER
ORIGINS

CONTENTS

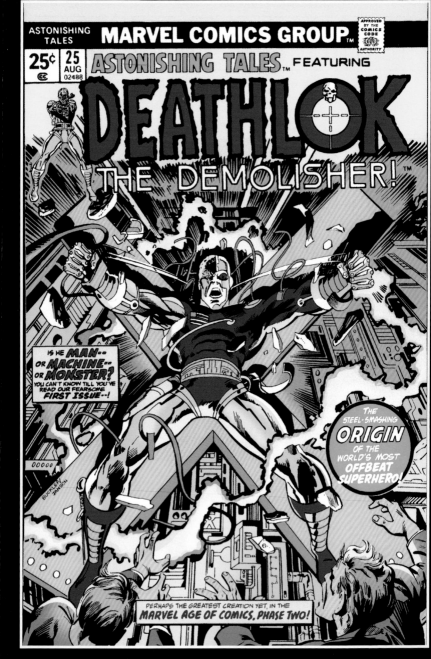

FIRE. REPEAT: FIRE.

NO. NOT YET. LET 'IM *SUFFER*. LET ME *SAVOR HIS FEAR*.

INCORRECT RESPONSE. UNACCEPTABLE. IMPLIES EMOTION; EMOTION PRE-CLUDED BY NATURE.

STUFF IT. I'M GONNA SEE 'IM SQUIRM. AND IF THAT'S EMOTION, IT'S THE ONLY ONE: *HATE* AND *CONTEMPT* FOR HIS FLESH-AND-BLOOD *GUTS*.

INSUBORDINATION TANTAMOUNT TO DYSFUNCTION. RE-PEAT: CONCLUDE PHASE ONE OF MIS-SION OR SUFFER DORMANCY.

FOR A COMPUTER, YOU *WORRY* TOO MUCH. YOU CAN'T SHUT ME OFF AND YOU *KNOW* IT. I'LL KILL HIM...JUST LET ME *ENJOY* IT.

SYNAPSE LAPSE SHALL BE OVERLOOKED UNTIL COMPLETION OF MISSION. PNEUMATIC LENSES ACTIVATED. OBSERVATIONS RECORDED:

GOD...

NO...

TARGET RUNS

STUMBLES

HELP...

FALLS

PLEASE...   DON'T...

CRAWLS BEGS WHIMPERS PLEADS GASPS RUNS

PLEASE...

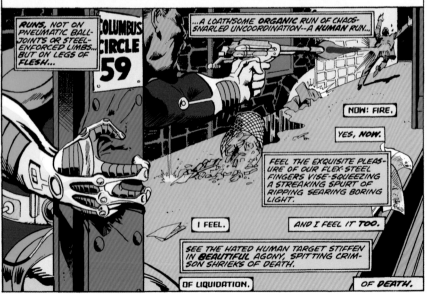

RUNS, NOT ON PNEUMATIC BALL-JOINTS OR STEEL-ENFORCED LIMBS, BUT ON LEGS OF FLESH...

COLUMBUS CIRCLE 59

...A LOATHSOME *ORGANIC* RUN OF CHAOS-SNARLED UNCOORDINATION--A *HUMAN RUN*...

NOW: FIRE.

YES, *NOW*.

FEEL THE EXQUISITE PLEAS-URE OF OUR FLEX-STEEL FINGERS VISE-SQUEEZING A STREAKING SPURT OF RIPPING SEARING BORING LIGHT.

I FEEL.   AND I FEEL IT *TOO*.

SEE THE HATED HUMAN TARGET STIFFEN IN *BEAUTIFUL* AGONY, SPITTING CRIM-SON SHRIEKS OF DEATH.

OF LIQUIDATION.   OF *DEATH*.

INTERNAL DISSIDENCE CANNOT BE TOLERATED--

SHUT UP AND TABULATE MY *PROGRESS!*

AND SINCE THEY WERE TO MEET DOWN HERE IN THE *SUBWAY,* THE OTHER PIGEON SHOULD BE JUST ABOUT *ARRIVING.*

CORRECT, BARRING VARIABLES OF--

PHASE ONE OF "MISSION: DOUBLE LIQUIDATION" CONCLUDED SUCCESSFULLY THROUGH UNORTHODOX METHODS,

TIME: 3:58 PM, SCHEDULED TIME OF TARGET'S RENDEZVOUS: 4:00 P.M.

--DETAINMENT.

YOU DON'T *BELONG* HERE, PRIVVIE, SO YOU *MUST* HAVE--

--MONEY.

WHY DID GILES INSIST ON MEETING *HERE*--IN THE MIDDLE OF A *SLUM-SCAVENGERS* JUNGLE--?!

SCAVENGERS WHO ARE ALSO *CANNIBALS--!*

THEIR BUSINESS WAS *IMPORTANT*--

--WHICH MEANS THE SECOND TARGET'LL BROOK NO *DELAY.*

CAN'T LET 'EM *STOP* ME!

GOTTA REACH THE *SUBWAY!*

THEY'RE SPRAWLED IN THE *GARBAGE.*

I *MADE* IT!

I'M *SAFE!*

I'M S--

SECOND TARGET LOCATED.

--A *PITY.* WE'VE *FAILED.* THE PATIENT'S *DEAD*--

--FOR ALL *INTENTS* AND *PURPOSES.*

BUT YOU *HAVE* ISOLATED A POR- TION OF HIS *BRAIN*--AND KEPT IT *ALIVE,* AS *ORDERED...?*

YES...AND I WON'T FOR- GET IT WAS *YOU* WHO ORDERED IT, RYKER.

YOU MAY DIS- PENSE WITH THE SANCTI- MONIOUS *HISTRIONICS,* DOCTOR.

COL. MANNING WAS THE MOST BRILLIANT MILI- TARY STRATEGIST *ALIVE*--AND I WANT THAT KNOWLEDGE *PRESERVED.*

PRESERVED. YES-- LIKE A FROZEN *VEGETABLE!*

RYKER, I WANT YOU TO KNOW YOU'VE INITIATED THE MOST GHOULISH SUR- GICAL PROCEDURE SINCE *FRANKENSTEIN.*

IN CASE YOU'RE NOT *AWARE* OF IT, MISTER, THERE'S BEEN A *WAR* GOING ON SINCE *1983.*

MANNING HERE WAS AWARE OF IT--*SO* AWARE OF IT THAT HE GOT *HALF* OF HIS *FACE* AND *ALL* OF HIS *RIGHT ARM* BLOWN OFF BY A *'CUSSION BOMB!*

AND IF WE'RE GOING TO *WIN* THIS WAR, WE NEED SOL- DIERS WHO *WON'T* GET SPLATTERED ALL OVER THE BATTLEFIELD!

WE NEED *SUPER- SOLDIERS*--MEN WITH BODIES OF *STEEL* AND MINDS OF COMPUTER- *PRECISION!* MEN WHO FUNCTION WITH THE IN- FALLIBILITY AND FEAR- LESSNESS OF *MACHINES!*

SO IF YOU'VE GOT ANY COMPLAINTS ABOUT WORKING ON *PROJECT: ALPHA- MECH,* DOCTOR, I SUG- GEST YOU BRING THEM UP AT YOUR *COURT- MARTIAL!*

LOOKS LIKE THE METAL-GRAFT WILL *TAKE*.

YEAH-- NO SIGNS OF IMMINENT *RE-JECTION*...

IN FACT, THE ENTIRE *OPERATION* SEEMS TO BE PROGRESSING WELL...

BUT IT'D PROGRESS A LOT *BETTER* WITHOUT *RYKER* CONSTANTLY SPY-ING ON US FROM HIS GLASS *CAGE*.

QUIET, WILKINS. HOW'S THE *MONITOR*, JIM?

ALL VITAL FUNCTIONS READ *STABLE*.

YOU KNOW, THERE'RE RUMORS THAT THIS ISN'T THE *FIRST* TIME *COMPUTER-HOUSING* HAS BEEN INSTALLED IN A *MAN*...

WELL, SEE THAT THOSE RUMORS NEVER LEAVE THIS *ROOM*--

--'CAUSE THERE ARE STILL *SOME* TAXPAYERS WHO WOULDN'T *LIKE* THE IDEA OF THE MILITARY SPENDING ITS TIME MAKING *MONSTERS*.

WHO *DE-SIGNED* THIS PROSTHET-IC ARM ANY-WAY?

TOP SECRET-- BUT IT'S SUPPOSED TO HAVE THE TENSILE STRENGTH OF *FORGED STEEL*...

...AND THE *GRIP* OF AN IRON *VISE*.

"*I'M GLAD THE REST* OF YOU HAVE THE *CA-PACITY FOR LEVITY*, DOCTORS--BECAUSE I FOR ONE CONSIDER THIS *BLASPHEMY*, EVEN IN THE *SECULAR* SENSE. THIS BEING IS *HIDEOUS*--

"--A *MOCKERY* OF MAN--AND BY RYKER'S DE-LIBERATE *SPECIFICATION*. PLASTIC SURGERY WOULD DIMINISH ITS PSYCHOLOGICAL POTENCY AS AN OBJECT OF *FEAR*, HE CLAIMED.

"AND THOUGH I'M LOATHE TO *PHRASE* IT THIS WAY, GENTLEMEN...IT APPEARS OUR OPERATION IS--

--*A SUCCESS*."

MISSION COMPLETE *SUCCESS*.

BOTH TARGETS HAVE BEEN *ELIMINATED* AS STIPULATED IN OUR *CONTRACT*.

VERY *GOOD*, DEATHLOK. I'M IM-*PRESSED*.

I AM PROCEEDING VIA *HELICRAFT* TO YOUR *OFFICES*, JULIAN BIGGS--

--YOU MAY *DEMONSTRATE* YOUR APPRECIATION ...IN *MONETARY* TERMS... WHEN I *ARRIVE*.

MY *OFFICES*--?! YOU DON'T EVEN KNOW WHERE THEY *ARE*--

THAT IS *INCORRECT*, JULIAN BIGGS, AS *I* SHALL SOON DE-MONSTRATE.

DESTINATION: ATTAINED.

DESCRIPTION: PARTIALLY CONSTRUCT-ED SKYSCRAPER; TOP FLOOR COM-PLETED IN ELABORATE DESIGN OF PENTHOUSE/FORTRESS.

INHABITED BY: JULIAN BIGGS, UNDERWORLD RACKETEER AND CURRENT EMPLOYER.

PROSPECTUS: POTENTIAL CONFLICT ORIGINATING FROM BIGGS' SURRO-GATES.

WHO'S *THIS* CHARACTER?

IT'S THAT *DEATHLOK* GUY THE BOSS HAD ME HIRE AS A *HIT-MAN*.

HOLD IT, UGLY.

PAUSE FOR IDENTIFICATION.

YOU'VE GOTTA HAVE AN *AP-POINTMENT* TO SEE MR. BIGGS--

I.D.'s TOO MUCH *TROUBLE*.

HEY! I SAID *HOLD* IT--!

ALERT: HOSTILITY.

MR. BIGGS HAS AUTHORIZED *ME* TO HANDLE ALL AFFAIRS CONCERNING *YOU*.

YOU GOT ANYTHING TO *REPORT*, YOU REPORT IT TO *ME*--

--'CAUSE THE BOSS DON'T WASTE *TIME* ON FREAK *MACHINES!*

EXTRAPOLATION: DANGER DANGER DANGER

AND *I* DON'T WASTE TIME ON *PUNK THUGS.*

ANGER

HESITATION

DANGER SUSPENDED--

WHY YOU STINKIN' UGLY *ROBOT*--!

--BY DESIRE TO PERSONALIZE VIOLENCE.

WE FEEL THE BEAUTY OF SOLENOID-ACTIVATED POWER CRUSHING SOFT FACE INTO PULPED FLESH AND BLOOD.

HE--HE *DEMOLISHED* HIS FACE--LIKE IT WAS *NOTHIN'!*

SPLUNCH!

SKRASH!

--*DEMOLISH* THAT STEEL GIRDER, *EFFORTLESSLY.* YES, HIS ARTIFICIAL ARM IS *MORE* THAN ADEQUATE.

BUT HE'S SO...*REPULSIVE.* JUST *LOOKING* AT HIM MAKES MY FLESH CRAWL. DO I *HAVE* TO WATCH THIS DEMONSTRATION WITH YOU, SIMON?

I SHOULD THINK YOU'D **WANT** TO SHARE THIS MOMENT WITH ME, NINA. IT'S THE FINEST OF MY **LIFE**-- A DREAM SCULPTED INTO **GLORY**...

IT ISN'T **EVERY** MAJOR WHO CAN DUPE THE ENTIRE **MILITARY** INTO FUNDING HIS PRIVATE **OBSESSION.** LISTEN--

ALL RIGHT, DOC-- GIVE US A **RUNDOWN** ON HIM.

VERY WELL, MAJOR RYKER. AS YOU KNOW, **PROJECT: ALPHAMECH** INVOLVES THE TECHNOLOGICAL **IMPROVEMENT** OF MAN. BY RETAINING A **SHRED** OF COL. LUTHER MANNING'S CONSCIOUSNESS-- SPECIFICALLY, THAT PORTION OF HIS **BRAIN** GOVERNING **STRATEGIC EXTRAPOLATIONS**--

Brain Fragment

SO **MUCH** OF MANNING'S FACE WAS DESTROYED, IN FACT, THAT WE'VE HAD TO VIRTUALLY **RECONSTRUCT** IT WITH **METAL** TO REPLACE THE PULVERIZED BONE.

Metal

Metal

--WE'VE BEEN ABLE TO ESTABLISH A BASIS FOR THE INTEGRATION OF MINIATURIZED **RELAY-CIRCUITS.** THESE CIRCUITS ARE PROTECTED BY A **STEEL PLATE** IMPLANTED IN THE **SKULL,** AND CONTROL-- AMONG OTHER FUNCTIONS--THE PNEUMATIC LENS WHICH SUBSTITUTES FOR MANNING'S DESTROYED EYE.

Circuits

Lens

THOSE SAME CIRCUITS ALSO ACTIVATE THE **AUDIO-RECEIVER** LOCATED IN-- AND COMPARABLE TO-- MANNING'S **EAR.** THE CYBORG'S **VOICE,** TOO, IS ELECTRONICALLY AMPLIFIED TO APPROXIMATE HUMAN SPEECH.

Receiver

Voice Box

"SWIVEL-SOCKET **BALL-JOINTS** AND PNEUMATIC **SPRINGS** IN THE CYBORG'S **LEGS** ENABLE HIM TO--

"--JUMP--

"--FORMIDABLE HEIGHTS WITH NO PERCEPTIBLE STRAIN--

"--TO HIS PHYSIOLOGICAL **COMPONENTS.**"

"MY COMPUTER-CODED ORDERS ARE FED **DIRECTLY** TO HIS DATA-PROCESSING CENTER--

"--ALONG WITH ALL **KNOWLEDGE** AND **INFORMATION** REQUIRED FOR THE SUCCESSFUL COMPLETION OF EACH MISSION.

"AND HIS MIND REMAINS **UNCLUTTERED** BY ANY EXTRANEOUS THOUGHT."

THANKS, DOC.

JUST **IMAGINE** WHAT I CAN **DO** WITH A BEING LIKE THIS, NINA--

--A BEING **TOTALLY SUBSERVIENT** TO **MY COMMAND!**

AND HE'S EQUIPPED FOR MORE THAN MERE *DEFENSE,* NINA...

THAT'S THE MOST SOPHISTICATED LASER-PISTOL *DEVELOPED.*

"*USED IN CONJUNCTION WITH COL. MANNING'S INSTINCTIVE STRATEGY AND BATTLE GRIT...*

"...*AS WELL AS A MORE BASIC WEAPON*--

"*--SUCH AS THAT MAGNETICALLY-ADHERING BAYONET...*

"...*NO ENEMY WILL BE ABLE TO*--"

--*KILL* YOU, GARGOYLE!

ALERT: DANGER.

TACTIC: BAYONET EMPLOYMENT.

THIS TIME I AIN'T HESITATING, 'PUTER!

TO DO SO WOULD PRECIPITATE DISAS--

TURN IT OFF, WILLYA! THAT BULLET RIPPED US!

YEAH--I FEEL IT.

IMPOSSIBLE. PAIN-CAPACITY OBVIATED BY INHERENT DESIGN--

--UNLIKE TARGET, WHICH HAS BEEN EXPUNGED WITH *GREAT* PAIN.

NO KIDDIN'.

FINAL TARGET ENACTING RETREAT MANEUVER.

YOU NEVER DID LIKE JOKES.

OUR FINAL *TARGET* OVER THERE, 'PUTER, IS A *JOKE*--

--ONE NOT EVEN WORTH THE *TIME* OF LIQUIDA-TION... WHETHER YOU *LIKE* 'IM OR *NOT.*

TERM 'LIKE' IMPLIES EMOTION...

...EMOTION ALIEN TO NATURE.

NO...PLEASE... IT--IT WASN'T *MY* IDEA TO ATTACK YOU. *PLEASE* DON'T--

--HURT ME...?

ALTHOUGH PENETRATION OF WALL ACCOM-PLISHED IN ELAPSED TIME OF 1.43 SECONDS--

--WALKING TO *DOOR* WOULD HAVE REQUIRED .16 SECONDS LESS.

SO SUE ME. MAY-BE I FELT LIKE *SHOWING OFF...*

...OR MAYBE I JUST FELT LIKE *KICKING A HOLE IN A WALL.*

CAPRICIOUSNESS INIMICAL TO--

*B*LOW IT OUT YOUR TRANSISTOR-IZED EAR.

*A*HEAD...CLAUSTROPHOBIA BOTTLING FREEDOM BOXING SQUEEZING NO AIR SUFFOCATING CAN'T BREATHE NO ROOM CAN'T MOVE CAUGHT CAGING IMPRISONING--

DOOR COM-POSED OF TEM-PERED STEEL, ANEALED WITH ADDITIONAL DEPOSITS OF UNALLOYED LEAD.

CALCULATED THICKNESS: NINE INCHES.

--INCHES *THICK*, DEATHLOK.

YOU'LL *NEVER* BE ABLE TO BATTER YOUR WAY THROUGH IT--

--BEFORE THE *ANESTHESIA* WE'VE INTRODUCED TO YOUR CHEMICAL "*BLOOD-STREAM*"--

--RENDERS YOU *DORMANT.*

SQUEEZING BOTTLING BOXING CLOSING CAGING STIFLING COMPRESSION OF SUFFOCATING TIGHTNESS NO ROOM NO ROOM NO ROOM NO ROOMMMMMMMMMMMM...

THOSE ELEC-TRONIC *DRAIN-LEADS* HOOKED TO THE COMPUTER SIPHON OFF HIS *ENERGY,* MAJOR, HE'LL BE *HELPLESS*--

EVEN *AFTER* HE'S REACTIVATED.

DEATHLOK-- CAN YOU *HEAR* ME?

AFFIRMATIVE.

WHY DID YOU FAIL TO COMPLY WITH PRO-GRAMMED *ORDERS*?

REPEAT QUESTION.

WHY DID YOU *REBEL*?

CAPACITY FOR REBELLION NONEXISTENT.

I *KNOW* THAT. SO WHY DID YOU *DO* IT?

QUESTION DEVOID OF LOGIC.

ANSWER IT *ANY-WAY,* BLAST IT!

IMPOSSIBLE; DOES NOT COMPUTE.

THEN YOU WEREN'T *AWARE* YOU WERE FLAGRANTLY DIS-OBEYING ORDERS--?

NOT *TRUE,* YOU POMPOUS BABOON. I WAS *WELL* AWARE OF IT.

YOUR *VOICE*--IT'S NOT THE *CYBORG* VOICE.

SURPRISE, SURPRISE.

IT'S *MANNING'S* VOICE!

YOU WERE EX-PECTING *ROBBIE THE ROBOT* MAYBE?

THIS IS *IMPOSSIBLE*--!

IT'S--IT'S AS THOUGH MANNING'S PERSONALITY WERE *REASSERTING* ITSELF--!

YOU EVEN *RECOG-NIZE* ME--?!

GOOD. IT'S ABOUT **TIME** WE GOT TO THE BOTTOM OF THIS BUSINESS AND I AIM TO **DO** IT.

NOW WHAT'S IT ALL **ABOUT?**

WELL, ACCORDING TO THESE **REPORTS,** SIR, THE CYBORG HAS SEVERELY **DYSFUNCTIONED.** HE **REBELLED** IN THE COURSE OF ONE OF HIS PROGRAMMED MISSIONS --**REFUSED** TO **COMPLETE** IT.

HE **DID,** EH?

WELL, HE'S AWAKE NOW **I'LL** SET HIM STRAIGHT.

MAJOR RYKER--THE COMPUTER'S GOING **WILD!**

IT WON'T **RESPOND**-- WE'RE LOSING **CONTROL!**

THE ENERGY FLOW'S BEEN **REVERSED**--IT'S BEING **SUCKED BACK** BY THE **CYBORG**--

AND IT'S BUILDIN' TO AN **OVERLOAD**... AS THOUGH HE'S GONNA BREAK--

SO'S THE THOUGHT OF A MAN **LOCKED IN DEATH** INHABITING THE BODY OF A **MACHINE.**

THAT'S ABOUT THE FREUDIAN **SIZE** OF IT, RYKER-BABES.

HOW COULD I FORGET MY OLD **BOOT-CAMP BUDDY...AND** THE SLIMY GHOUL WHO TURNED ME INTO A GOBLIN'S ANSWER TO **GENGHIS KHAN?**

"--LOOSE!"

RED ALERT: PROJECT ALPHA-MECH CYBORG DEATHLOK HAS ESCAPED TO ROOF HELIPORT.

WARNING: CYBORG BERSERK. APPREHEND AT ALL COSTS. REPEAT: RED ALERT--

HE'S RIPPED-OFF A BLOODY HELICOPTER --FIFTY GRAND'S WORTH OF U.S. GOVERNMENT PROPERTY... RIGHT IN FRONT OF OUR NOSES!

AIN'T NOTHIN' CAN STOP 'IM!

NOTHIN'S GONNA STOP ME, 'PUTER--!

NOT EVEN NINE INCHES OF SOLID STEEL--

--WHEN IT STANDS BETWEEN ME AND A HUNDRED-THOUSAND BUCKS!

ALL RIGHT, BIGGS--I OFFED YOUR TWO PIGEONS.

WHERE'S MY MONEY?

MONEY?

WHAT DOES A MACHINE NEED MONEY FOR?

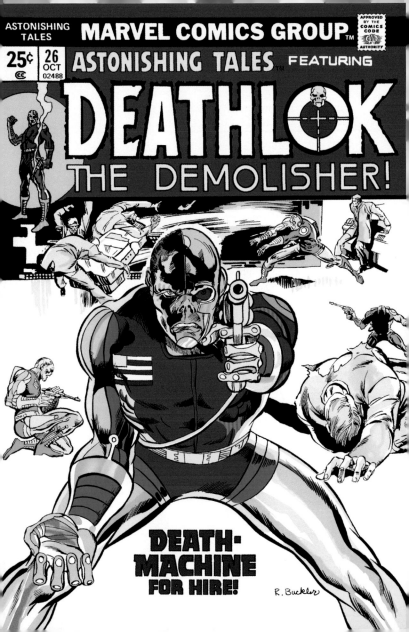

SO WHY DIDN'T YA **SAY** SO?!

WOULDA HAD A LITTLE MORE TIME TO **DUCK**, AT LEAST.

BALLISTIC TRAJECTORY TERMINATED IN IMPACT WITH PRESSURE-BOMB LOCATED WITHIN BUILDING.

YA DON'T **SAY.**

RESULT: EXPLOSION OF CONSIDERABLE MAGNITUDE.

NO **KIDDIN'**...

...I NEVER WOULDA **GUESSED** IT, 'PUTER.

GUESS THE BOMB WAS PLANTED FOR **ME**--IN CASE THE SNIPER **MISSED.**

WHICH HE **DID**... 'CEPT HE HIT THE BOMB **INSTEAD.**

A REAL **WINNER**, THAT SNIPER...

SPEAKIN' OF WHICH, WONDER WHY THE MORON HASN'T POPPED OFF ANOTHER **SHOT**...

NOT THAT IT WOULD DO 'IM ANY **GOOD** AGAINST A **CYBORG.**

SUBJECT ASSAILANT HAS ABANDONED WEAPON.

WELL I'LL BE A MONITOR'S UNCLE--

--THE JERK'S AS YELLOW AS A BABY **CHICKEN.**

EXTRAPOLATION: SUBJECT'S POSITION DICTATES A COURSE OF RETREAT ACROSS ROOF TO ADJACENT BUILDING'S ROOF.

WELL, 'PUTER, WE'LL JUST SEE--

--ABOUT THAT.

SO THE BACK-SHOOTER'S RUNNIN' ACROSS THE ROOF OF *THIS* BUILDING...

--IF THE ROOF HE'S **ON**--

...AND HE WANTS TO JUMP ONTO THE ROOF OF THE BUILDING *NEXT DOOR*.

--JUST SUDDENLY--

--DECIDES TO--

--*COLLAPSE*.

BUT SEEMS TO ME HE JUST CAN'T *DO* THAT--

MEMORY SYNAPSE-LOCK IDENTIFIES SUBJECT AS--

I ALREADY *RECOGNIZE* 'IM, 'PUTER.

HE'S ONE OF THE SLIMY JERKS WHO KIDNAPPED MIKE IN THE 'COPTER...

...THE 'COPTER I TRACED *HERE*-- WITH THE SENSORS IN *MY* 'COPTER.

CORRECT: ALBEIT EVIDENCE OF HELI-COPTER'S PROXIMITY NONEXISTENT.

LOOK, 'PUTER--IF THE SENSORS *SAY* IT'S AROUND HERE, IT'S *AROUND* HERE.

CONCLUSION DEVOID OF LOGIC ATTRIBUTABLE TO POSSIBILITY THAT--

SHUT UP. SOMETHIN' *ELSE* JUST OCCURRED TO ME--I RECOGNIZE THIS GUY FROM *SOME-WHERE ELSE* TOO...FROM *RYKER'S JOINT*...

...FROM THE TIME THEY CALLED ME IN FOR *INTERROGATION*...

--CALLED IN FOR--

--INTERROGATION--

--REGARDING--

SALINE COMPOSITION STABILIZING FUZZY MUZZY VAGUE NULLIFIED CHEMICAL DORMANCY BLOODSTREAM CLEANSED RUSHING FILLING VEINS AND HATED HUMAN FLESH WITH AWARENESS BURSTING OPEN CLOUDS SHREDDING BEFORE SUN NEW DAY AWAKENING CONSCIOUSNESS RETURNING BUDDING AWAKE.

--A POSSIBLE *DYSFUNCTION*, PETERS.

SEEMS THE CYBORG HAS DEMONSTRATED TENDENCIES TOWARD REBELLION AGAINST THE COMPUTER INSTALLED WITHIN HIS *CHEST CAVITY*...

WE'VE GOT REPORTS HERE OF HIS LAST TWO MISSIONS. ON *FOUR* SEPARATE OCCASIONS HE'S DISREGARDED PROGRAMMED *ORDERS*--ON *ONE* OCCASION HE'S *DEFIED* A DIRECT ORDER-- AND *TWICE* HE'S ACTED *COUNTER* TO PROGRAMMING...

...AND SEEMINGLY OF HIS *OWN VOLITION*.

NOW I KNOW THAT'S *IMPOSSIBLE*, BUT ONCE HE *COMES TO*, I WANT TO QUESTION HIM *ANYWAY*--AND I *DON'T* WANT ANY *TROUBLE*, PETERS.

IS THAT SUPPOSED TO MEAN I SHOULD *YAWN*?

ALERT: HUMAN PERSONALITY REASSERTING ITSELF. REPRESS IMMEDIATELY BEFORE--

TOO LATE. ALL THREE OF US ARE HERE IN CORRUPT MOCKERY OF FLESH BLOOD GUTS CIRCUITS WIRES CONFUSED UGLY PROFANE PERVERTED WANT OUT CAN'T STAY TOO CROWDED NO CONTROL CHAOS CONFUSION HORRIBLE CROWDING MORE AND MORE.

THERE WON'T BE ANY TROUBLE, MAJOR RYKER.

THE *ANESTHESIA* WE'VE INTRODUCED TO HIS CHEMICAL BLOODSTREAM WILL KEEP HIM GROGGY...

...AND THE ELECTRONIC *DRAIN-LEADS* HOOKED TO HIS COMPUTER ARE SIPHONING OFF HIS *ENERGY*. HE'LL BE *HELPLESS*--

--EVEN *AFTER* HE'S REACTIVATED.

[27]

MIND-FREEZE DISTORTED MEMORY-SWIRL THOUGHTS CHURNING FRENZY OF PREVIOUS IMPRESSIONS WARPED BY EMOTION AND PASSAGE OF TIME-LURCHED CATHARSIS REMEMBERED FROM BEFORE MORE VIVID NOW MORE EFFECT MORE POWER MORE HATE HATE HATE

I'M *ALREADY* AWAKE, YOU STUPID *BABOONS!*

WHAT THE--?!!

THAT'S *LUTHER MANNING'S* VOICE COMING OUT OF THE *DEATHLOK CYBORG--!*

SO WHO'D YA *EXPECT,* RYKER-BABES--

--*DORIS DAY* MAYBE?

THIS IS *IMPOSSIBLE--!*

MAJOR RYKER-- THE COMPUTER'S GOING *WILD!*

THE ENERGY FLOW'S BEEN *REVERSED*--IT'S BEING *SUCKED BACK* BY THE *CYBORG*--

IT WON'T *RESPOND*--WE'RE LOSING *CONTROL!*

--AND IT'S BUILDING TO AN *OVERLOAD*...AS THOUGH HE'S GOING TO BREAK--

"--*FREE!*"

YOU BET YOUR SWEET *BRASS* I'M FREE.

NO--!

STAY *BACK* --GET *AWAY* FROM ME--!

SURE.

RIGHT AFTER I *PAY YOU BACK* FOR--

--TURNIN' ME INTO A *MACHINE*.

NOW, IF YOU'LL FORGIVE MY *MANNERS*, I GOTTA *SPLIT*.

GOT SOMETHIN' TO *DO*--

--SOMETHIN' TO *DO* BEFORE *SPLITTIN'* THIS PLACE.

WARNING: PRESENCE OF NOW-DETONATED BOMB INDICATES TRAP.

YES, BUT THAT *BODY*... LOOKS LIKE--

--MIKE...?

INCORRECT. ALTHOUGH IDENTITY OF CORPSE UNKNOWN, IT IS NOT MIKE TRAVERS.

ALL RIGHT, SO IT'S *NOT MIKE*-- BUT YOUR MEMORY TAPES ARE *SLIPPIN'*, 'PUTER...

...IF YOU DON'T RECOGNIZE THIS GUY AS ANOTHER ONE OF *RYKER'S GOON'S*.

WAITAMINUTE-- I *SMELL* SOMETHIN'...

IMPOSSIBLE; OLFACTORY SENSE OBSOLETE BY NATURE.

THEN HOWCUM I SMELL *DEAD FLESH*--

--AS WELL AS SOME OF THE *LIVING* VARIETY?

IMPOSSIBLE SCENT OF DEAD FLESH ATTRIBUTABLE TO NATURE OF REFRIGERATED ROOM: STOREHOUSE FOR BLACK MARKET MEAT.

REFRIGERATOR

YEAH-- AND THE *LIVING* ODOR'S COMIN' FROM RYKER'S BLACK MARKET *ASSASSINS*.

SITUATION REPORT: SUBJECT EQUIPPED WITH MACHINEGUN CAPABLE OF DISCHARGING THREE BULLETS PER SECOND.

SITUATION REPORT: MAJOR THREAT ELIMINATED...

OTHER SUBJECTS LAUNCHING OFFENSIVE.

...BUT ONE IN THE RIGHT SPOT *COULD* PUT ME OUT FOR A *WHILE*...

--BETTER TAKE 'EM OUT *FAST.*

SITUATION REPORT: THREE ASSAILANTS SUCCESSFULLY LIQUIDATED. TWO REMAIN EXTANT.

I KNOW HOW YOU HATE TO BE **CORRECTED,** 'PUTER--

--BUT CHALK **ANOTHER** ONE AND LOG THE TALLY AT **FOUR** DOWN AND **ONE** TO GO.

ADJUSTMENT NOTED AND LOGGED.

SWIVEL-SOCKET BALL JOINTS PUMPING SPEED PREVIOUS KNEE DAMAGE EFFECTING MINIMAL DELAY BULLETS BLISTERING AIR WHIPPING FRENZY RACING RACING BULLETS WHINING SHRIEKING--

--RACING BULLETS SLICING AIR BLISTERING EARS RACING BALL-JOINTS CHURNING SPEED ESCAPE FLIGHT RYKER'S MEN BEHIND.

GOTTA GET **OUTTA** HERE BEFORE THAT STINKIN' **COMPUTER** TAKES OVER AGAIN.

DOOR AHEAD--MAYBE THE WAY OUT--!

NO.

BUT TOO LATE TO BACK UP **NOW.**

CRASH OUT THE **WINDOW** ACROSS ROOM...

HUH--?!

THE **DEATHLOK** CYBORG--?!

LUTHER-- LUTHER MANNING!

MIKE?

MIKE TRAVERS --?!

THEY GOT *YOU* PLAYIN' WITH COMPUTER TAPES--?!

THEY'LL *BRAIN-WASH* YOU, MIKE --THEY'LL PROGRAM YOUR *BRAIN.*

LUTHER, I DON'T KNOW *HOW* YOU GOT YOUR OWN *HEAD* BACK--

--BUT YOU'VE *GOT* TO REALIZE THAT *YOU'VE BEEN PROGRAMMED!*

YEAH, I *REMEM-BER.*

THEY SHOVE COMPUT-ER CARDS RIGHT INTO THIS SLOT IN MY *ARM...*

BUT THEY'VE DONE IT FOR THE *LAST TIME,* MIKE --

I AIN'T *NOBODY'S* BLOODY MACHINE--

--AND AIN'T *NO MORE ORDERS* GONNA BE PLUGGED INTO MY *ARM--OR MY BRAIN!!!*

HE WENT IN *HERE..*.

QUIET NOW...

IN FACT, I'M GONNA RIP OUT THIS WHOLE STINKIN' *COMPUTER-COMPLEX--*

LUTHER--!

--OUTSIDE THE *DOOR!*

GUNS...?

DON'T WORRY, MIKE-- *I'LL* PROTECT YOU FROM THESE LUNATICS--

--RAM THEIR LOUSY ORDER-MAKIN' *COMPUTER* DOWN THEIR SMELLY *THROATS!*

LUTHER-- WHAT ARE YOU *DOING?!*

THEY'RE ON *OUR* SIDE--!

TRY TO TAKE HIM *ALIVE--*

--BUT DON'T HESITATE TO *KILL* IF YOU HAVE TO!

WHAT'S GOING *ON* HERE--?

YOU CAN'T *SHOOT* AT US--!!!

NOW *YOU'VE* GOTTA REALIZE, MIKE--

--THEY'RE *CRAZY.*

AND WHETHER YOU *LIKE* IT OR *NOT--*

DYSFUNCTION. REPEAT: DYSFUNCTION. DESIST PRESENT COURSE OF ACTION IMMEDIATELY OR SUFFER DEACTIVATION.

TERRIFIC. STUPID *COMPUTER'S* ACTIN' UP AGAIN.

HEY *LISTEN,* 'PUTER--*SHUT UP,* WILLYA...

...WHILE I DUMP MY *BULLET-SHIELD* ON THE NEW RECRUITS *BELOW.*

ANYWAY, YOU OUGHTTA *KNOW* BY NOW THAT YOU *CAN'T* TURN ME OFF.

WELL, WHADDAYA KNOW--*RYKER'S* DOWN THERE, TOO.

BETTER JUMP IN THE 'COPTER AND TAKE *OFF.*

I'LL *GET* YOU, DEATHLOK-- AND *YOU* TOO, TRAVERS--!

I'LL *GET YOU BOTH--!*

WE ALREADY GOT *TRAVERS,* DEATHLOK...

...AND NOW *I'M* GONNA GET *YOU--!*

FINAL ASSAILANT ALIGNED WITH MEAT-HOOK RAIL.

GOOD IDEA, 'PUTER.

UHHN--!

SLID IT RIGHT INTO A BINGO-BULLSEYE.

MY *BACK--!*

GOD, MY *BACK...*

AWRIGHT, SWEETIE, BEFORE I *ZAP* YA--*SPILL IT!* WHERE'S *TRAVERS?*

IN THE *BACK ROOM?*

NO...

STATUE...

...LIBER...

...HUG-K-K...

FINAL ASSAILANT LIQUIDATED.

YEAH.

AN' I DIDN'T EVEN KNOW I'D *DONE* IT...

SORTA TAKES THE *SATISFACTION* OUT'VE IT.

AND ON TOP OF *THAT,* MIKE ISN'T EVEN *HERE.*

THIS WAS ALL A *SET-UP. A TRAP.*

AND *THAT MAKES ME--*

--MAD!

PROPOSED COURSE OF ACTION: UTILIZATION OF STOLEN HELICOPTER STATIONED OUTSIDE.

DESTINATION: STATUE OF LIBERTY, 2.3 MILES FROM PRESENT LOCATION.

LOOK, 'PUTER, I'M THE ONE WHO SET THE COURSE--SO WHY DON'T YOU TELL ME SOMETHING I DON'T KNOW...?

F'RINSTANCE--A READOUT ON MY *KNEE.*

PROBABILITY OF INFECTION NEGATED BY DEPLOYMENT OF CHEMICAL ANTIBODIES TO SOURCE OF LACERATION. REGENERATIVE PROCESS INITIATED.

FIGURES. I COULDN'T HURT MYSELF IF I *WANTED* TO.

--IF I *WANTED* TO, MIKE. YOU REALIZE WHAT THAT *MEANS--?*

I'M ALMOST *IMMORTAL,* MIKE-- I CAN DO ALMOST *ANYTHING.*

MAYBE SO, LUTHER, BUT IF YOU'LL FORGIVE ME FOR *SAYING* SO... THERE'S A LOT YOU'VE GOT TO *LEARN.*

YOU'VE BEEN *REBORN*--ALMOST LIKE A *BABY.* YOU'RE *NAIVE...* YOU DON'T UNDERSTAND WHAT IT IS TO BE A *CYBORG.*

ALL RIGHT, MIKE--WE'LL LAND THE 'COPTER ON THIS ROOF, COOK UP SOME *FOOD,* AND YOU CAN CLUE ME ON THE *BIRDS 'N BEES.*

WARNING: ROOFTOP DECEPTIVE IN SAFETY-FACTOR--ACTUALLY VULNERABLE TO ENCROACHMENT OF--

OKAY, WE'RE *SAFE* UP HERE, MIKE.

NOW WHAT'S THIS ABOUT BEING A *BABY*?

LUTHER, YOU SIMPLY DON'T KNOW WHAT A CYBORG *IS*.

BUT *I* WORKED IN RYKER'S *LAB*. I KNOW WHAT *HAPPENED* TO YOU...

SHUT *UP*, 'PUTER!

REMEMBER WHEN WE WERE *ARMY BUDDIES*, LUTHER? *BEST FRIENDS*...?

...HOW WE'D ALWAYS *STUCK TOGETHER* DURING THE *WAR-GAMES*...?

...AND HOW I *SAVED* YOUR *LIFE* DURING ONE OF THE GAMES--

--ONLY TO SEE YOU BLASTED BY A *'CUSSION BOMB* TEN MINUTES *LATER*...?

YOU NEVER *REVIVED*, LUTHER. YOU'RE...*DEAD*.

ALERT: DANGER. OFFENSIVE LAUNCHED BY HUMANOID CANNIBALS.

UHNN--!

WHY DIDN'T YOU *SAY* THAT'S WHAT THE DANGER WAS--INSTEAD O' FLAPPIN' YER JAW-CIRCUITS FOR *EXERCISE*?

REAL EFFICIENT, KNOW WHAT I MEAN?

HEY--WHAT'S HAPPENIN' OVER THERE WITH MIKE--?! THOSE AREN'T *CANNIBALS*--!

CORRECT. MEMORY-SYNAPSE IDENTIFIES THEM AS EMPLOYEES OF--

--MAJOR SIMON RYKER.

HEY, *SLIMY*--

--GET YER FILTHY *TEETH*--

--OUTTA MY *KNEE*!

THOSE STINKIN' *SNAKES* KID-NAPPED MIKE--!

AN' ME WITH A BUM *KNEE*...

CANNIBALS WERE NOTHIN' BUT A *DIVERSION*...

CORRECT.

WELL, GUESS I CAN USE THE 'COP-TER'S *SENSORS*--

--TO *TRACE* 'EM.

STUPID IDEA FOR US TO USE THE *SENSORS*--

--WHEN ALL THEY HADDA DO WAS PLANT A *DECOY* IN THE *MEAT PLANT.*

CORRECT.

WELL, THERE SHE *IS.* THE OLE LADY AIN'T WHAT SHE *USED* TO BE...

BUT THEN--NEITHER AM I--

--AND TARZAN AIN'T GOT *NOTHIN'* ON ME!

IT'S THAT CYBORG, *DEATHLOK!*

HE'S *FOUND* US--AND THAT MEANS RYKER'S ORDERS TO *KILL* GO INTO EFFECT--

--*NOW!*

FEEL SPURTING DEATH SLICING THROUGH SCARLET-RIPPED HATED HUMAN FLESH DESTROYING KILLING SLASHING CUTTING BEAUTY.

Y'KNOW, 'PUTER, I BEEN *WONDERING*--IS IT *YOU* OR *ME* WHO CONTRIBUTES THE *SICK STREAK* TO OUR *THIRD PERSONALITY*...?

BOTH.

[38]

HURRY, MAN-- *HURRY!*

I HEAR HIM *OUTSIDE*--HE *KNOWS* WE'RE HERE IN THE *STATUE*--

--AND IT *MUST* BE READY BY THE TIME HE *GETS* HERE!

ALL RIGHT, *CREAMPUFFS*--

--I *KNOW* MIKE TRAVERS IS *IN* THERE...

MIKE AN' ME WERE *ARMY BUDDIES,* Y'KNOW...

...*BEST FRIENDS...*

HE EVEN *SAVED MY LIFE* ONCE...WHEN I WAS STILL *ALIVE...*

SO YOU CAN SEE *WHY*--

--NOTHIN'S GONNA *STOP* ME--

WARNING: PRESENT COURSE OF ACTION RECKLESS--

--FROM EVENING THE *SCORE*--

--ALL LOGIC SYSTEMS INDICATE DANGER OF *TRAP.*

BY BUSTIN' HIM *OUT!*

EMOTIONS OVERRIDING LOGIC. REPEAT: DANGER, ALL PROBABILITY DATA INDICATES--

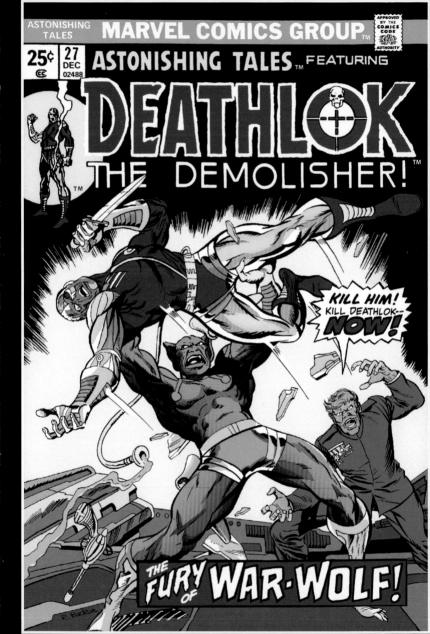

THE PREPARATIONS ARE NEAR COMPLETION, RYKER.

THAT'S **MAJOR** RYKER, DOCTOR, AND OUR TIME HAS JUST ABOUT RUN OUT...

SO SPLIT! AND I MEAN NOW!

THINGS ARE GOING TO START FLYING ANY MINUTE!

SITUATION: THREE TARGETS EXPUNGED. FOUR EXTANT. PROBABILITY OF DAMAGE.

YOU TRYING TO TELL ME A BULLET OR TWO--

--MIGHT TAKE ME OUT 'PUTER? **NO WAY!**

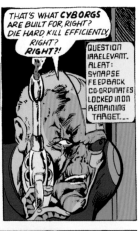

THAT'S WHAT **CYBORGS** ARE BUILT FOR, RIGHT? DIE HARD, KILL EFFICIENTLY, RIGHT? **RIGHT?!**

QUESTION IRRELEVANT. ALERT: SYNAPSE FEEDBACK CO-ORDINATES LOCKED IN ON REMAINING TARGET...

PREPARE TO FIRE!

REPEAT: FIRE!

YES **FIRE!**

WARNING: INTER-SPECIFIC AGGRESSION MAY BECOME EXTREMLY DANGEROUS...

YEAH, IT'S ALREADY CAUSED SIX HUMAN DEATHS...

AND I'M GONNA BE SPILLING MORE BLOOD BEFORE THIS IS OVER, 'PUTER!

DOMINATING MOTIVATING PERSONALITY FORCING DECISIONS. THRUSTING WILL, HUMAN DRIVES BEING DRIVEN, DIDACTIC HUMAN THINKING SUBVERSIVE TO COMPUTER'S LOGISTICS SYSTEMS GETTING STRONGER WINNING, WINNING...

SHOVE YOUR PRIME DIRECTIVES! MIKE'S IN THERE...

SHUT UP! I'M GOIN' IN AND SAVE HIM NOW NO MATTER **WHAT!**

SITUATION REPORT: ENVIRONMENT INIMICAL. POSSIBILITIES OF TRAP 99.998% PRIMARY DIRECTIVE---

REPEAT: PRIME DIRECTIVE IS SELF-PRESERVATION AT ALL COST. DANGER INHERENT--- REPEAT.

DANGER, DANGER, DANGER! ALL PROBABILITY DATA INDICATES---

[45]

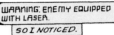

IN A QUANDRY, COMPUTER PUSH-BUTTON PULSES SCREAMING TO BE HEARD, HUMAN EMOTION OVERRIDING ALL LOGIC...

NO!

IT CAN'T END THIS WAY, NOT NOW, NOT YET. *IT'S NOT HOW I PLANNED IT--!*

--NOT QUITE TURNING OUT LIKE WE PLANNED IT, HEY, BUDDY?

MIKE, YOU TALK TOO MUCH.

IF YOU'D TALK LESS AND *SHOOT STRAIGHTER* WE'D BE OUT OF THIS STUPID "TRAINING SESSION."

YEAH, THEN WHERE WOULD WE BE?

I DUNNO, THESE *WAR GAMES* SEEM SO REAL. SOMETIMES I GET THIS CREEPY FEELING *THIS* IS *THE REAL THING!*

KNOW WHAT YOU MEAN, LUTHER, IT'S NOT LIKE *'NAM*, THE WAY *DAD* DESCRIBED IT.

YOU'RE WRONG THERE, MIKE. IN A WAY IT IS. THE ENEMY IS UNSEEN *HERE*, TOO. THE ONLY THING IS, THE *WEAPONS* HAVE CHANGED *MEN* ARE STILL THE SAME.

YEAH, YOU KNOW, I DON'T THINK I'LL *EVER* GET THE HANG OF THESE "JAMMERS."

CAN'T WAIT 'TILL THEY ISSUE THE NEW LASERS AS STANDARD EQUIPMENT.

YOU'RE A LOT LIKE YOU'RE OL' MAN, MIKE. HE WAS ALWAYS IMPATIENT, ALWAYS FASCINATED BY THE TECHNICAL SIDE OF THINGS.

BETTER *CAN* THAT KIND OF TALK, LUTHER.

"BIG BROTHER" MAYBE LISTENING IN.

RYKER'S GOT "EYES" AND "EARS" EVERYWHERE, YOU KNOW.

BUT I'VE WONDERED MORE'N A FEW TIMES--WHAT IF ALL THE COMPUTERS RUNNING THIS "WAR", ALL THE FANCY WEAPONS AND STUFF ARE JUST AN EXCUSE FOR KEEPING *US BUSY* AND THE *FAT CATS* COMFORTABLE.

SPEAKING OF *MISTER EGO*

WHEN YOU TWO FINISH YOUR LITTLE STROLL MAYBE WE CAN GO THROUGH SOME *REAL* WAR MANEUVERS!

DOUBLE TIME, SOLDIERS! DON'T YOU KNOW AN *ORDER* WHEN YOU HEAR IT?

I *HEARD* IT, RYKER. STILL TRYING TO MAKE IT TO MAJOR?

CLIMBING ON EVERYBODY'S BACK, HUH? WELL, I AIN'T *IMPRESSED*, CAPTAIN!

ARE YOU FINISHED?

THEN... *LET...ME...HAVE...MY...SAY.*

I'M STILL *COMMANDING OFFICER* HERE. SO *STRAIGHTEN UP!* NOW!

YOU'RE BOTH RUNNING THE *OBSTACLE COURSE* WITHOUT HELMET OR GEAR. IF THERE'S ANY "*MAN*" IN EITHER OF YOU, WE'LL FIND OUT, OUT THERE. NOW *MOVE!*

LUTH, WATCH YOUR STEP... OH GOD!

HUH?

SORRY, BUT THIS IS FOR YOUR *OWN GOOD!*

JUST MISSED THAT MINE, OL' BUDDY... UMPH!

--MISSED TARGET BY WIDE MARGIN. REALIGN SIGHT AND CORRECT AIM--

THERE'S NOTHING WRONG WITH MY AIM, 'PUTER. I HIT WHAT I WANTED.

SITUATION: OPPONENT'S LASER DESTROYED.

EXTRAPULATION: WILL LAUNCH PHYSICAL ATTACK.

JUST SHUT UP, WILL YA? LET ME THINK MY WAY OUTTA THIS ONE...

HOW? HOW COULD YOU DO IT, RYKER?

DO WHAT? TURN MIKE TRAVERS INTO THE THING HE NOW IS? SIMPLE.

I USE PEOPLE TO CREATE THE FUTURE. MY ULTIMATE GOAL IS TO GAIN MASTERY OVER LIFE--AND FINALLY, DEATH.

WAR WOLF IS MY FIRST SUCCESSFUL CYBORG. YOU, DEATHLOK, WERE ONE OF MY UNFORTUNATE FAILURES!

READ OUT: CYBORG OPPONENT, ACCORDING TO PROBABILITY ANALYSIS HAS STRENGTH OF TWENTY MEN--

SO WHAT AM I SUPPOSED TO DO? I CAN'T KILL HIM--

I'LL BE KILLING MIKE!

IRRELEVANT. SIGHT RE-ALIGNED ON TARGET--

PREPARE TO FIRE AT MAXIMUM SETTING--NOW.

I--I CAN'T DO IT.

I CAN'T... SHOOT... DOWN... MIKE...

WARNING:

REFUSAL TO ACT--

--WILL RESULT IN OUR DESTRUCTION.

[49]

UNNNN! SO *LET* IT. I'D BE BETTER OFF *DEAD!*

ANOMALY. PRESENT ACTION SELF-DE-STRUCTIVE IN NATURE. TOTALLY ILLOGICAL.

SO'S BEING *LOCKED* IN *DEATH*, FORCED TO PLAY VERBAL VOLLEY BALL WITH A *COMPUTER*.

TELL ME SOME THING *NEW!*

DISPARAGING TERMINAL EYES RECORD IMAGES FLASHING OF HUNDREDS OF SKULL'S WITH ENDLESS ROWS OF TEETH, SOCKETS YAWNING BLACK HOLES PROMISING HOLY DEATH, ESCAPE IMPOSSIBLE, DEATH THE ONLY RELEASE.

GREAT. WHILE I'M GETTIN' BUSTED UP, SOME DISTANT PART OF MY BRAIN IS ACTUALLY *ENJOYING* THIS.

READ-OUT: DAMAGE TO PERIPHERAL UNITS. OPERATING UNDER CRIPPLE-MODE CONDITIONS.

SCANNING FOR POSSIBLE ROUTES OF ESCAPE.

GOOD *THINKING*, 'PUTER. AND JUST WHAT HAVE I GOT TO ESCAPE *TO* ?

DEPRESSIVE DYSPHORIC FEELING, IDEATION, RESULTING FROM RUNNING HYSTERICAL FEAR OF DYING, ONLY THOUGHT OF ESCAPE, CAN'T THINK LOGICALLY, MUST GET OUT, OUT--

WARNING: DAMAGING BLOW HAS LOOSENED LIFE-LINE VALVE--

DROP-DEAD HALT IMMINENT.

REPEAT: SEVERING OF VITAL LIFE-LINE HAS INITIATED FLESH DETERIORATION.

LIFE FLUIDS DRAINING.

OH MY GOD!

SUPPORT SYSTEM AT HALF CAPACITY. SITUATION CRITICAL.

KILL HIM *SLOWLY,* MY WAR-WOLF. I WANT TO *SAVOR* THIS MOMENT.

YES, YES! JUST AS I HAD THE POWER TO CREATE PROJECT *ALPHA·MECH* AND YOU, DEATHLOK--

--SO DO I HAVE THE POWER TO *DESTROY* YOU.

EMERGENCY VALVE SHUT--OFF EFFECTED. FLUID LOSS IS ESTIMATED 31.29.

SO I LOOK A *LITTLE UGLIER--*

--I STILL GOT SOME *FIGHT* LEFT IN ME!

AND I'LL TAKE RYKER DOWN A PEG OR TWO BEFORE I *WINK OUT.*

THIS IS WHAT I'VE WAITED FOR.

YOU GROVELING *BEFORE* ME. YOU WERE A *FOOL* TO BELIEVE WHAT I SAID, DEATHLOK.

IT ONLY *AIDED* ME IN DEFEATING YOU. I *LIED* ABOUT MIKE TRAVERS--

HE *DIED* ON THE *OPERATING TABLE.* NOW YOU BOTH HAVE MET YOUR JUST *END--!*

YOU JUST TOLD ME THE ONE *THING.*

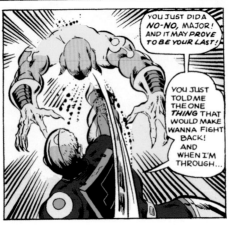

YOU JUST DID A *NO-NO,* MAJOR! AND IT MAY *PROVE TO BE YOUR LAST!*

YOU JUST TOLD ME THE ONE *THING* THAT WOULD MAKE WANNA FIGHT BACK! AND WHEN I'M THROUGH...

...I HAVE A SCORE TO SETTLE WITH *YOU!*

NO!

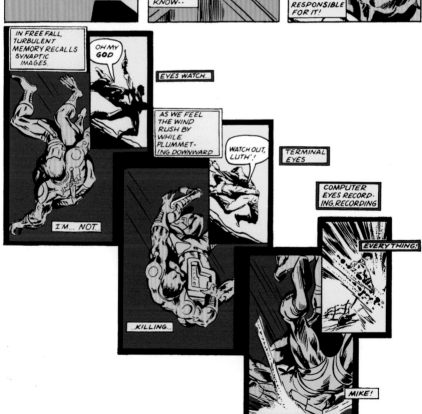

OPPONENT'S MAIN CIRCUITS NEAR DEAD HALT.

UH-UH.

HE AIN'T KICKIN' OFF UNTIL I'M THROUGH WITH HIM!

ANOMALY: EMOTION DISRUPTING PERIPHERAL UNITS. TERMINATION OF CYBORG FOE--

SHOULD BE DONE WITHOUT ME ENJOYING IT, RIGHT?

IF I COULD KILL WITH HATE I'D COMMIT GENOCIDE! BUT IT'S RYKER I'M UP AGAINST--

ANOMALY: REVENGE IS NOT A PART OF PROGRAMMING. A MACHINE HAS NO MOTIVE-- ONLY PURPOSE.

YOU JUST HIT ON SOMETHIN', 'PUTER.

I'M AN ALPHA-MECH CYBERNETIC MOBILE UNIT. I'M PROGRAMMED TO KILL, RIGHT? MY PURPOSE, MY ONE PURPOSE FOR EXISTENCE--

--IS TO KILL!

READOUT: CYBORG OPPONENT DEMOLISHED. THREAT OF RYKER STILL EXTANT.

RYKER'LL KEEP...

RIGHT NOW, TOO WEAK TO CLIMB UP THERE. GET... 'COPTER... DOWN.

'COPTER ON AUTO CO-ORDINATES, LANDING AS PROGRAMMED

LIKE AN ELECTRIC BUZZ THAT'S ALWAYS THERE. YOU NEVER NOTICE IT 'TIL IT STOPS.

THE "VOICE" YOU REFER TO IS AN IMPLANT IN THE CIRCUITS OF OUR MAIN COMPUTER COMPLEX.

WELL, WHY DIDN'T YOU TELL ME THAT BEFORE? I WAS BE GINING TO THINK I WAS SICKO.

YOU NEVER ASKED.

I NEVER ASKED.

HOW ABOUT TRACING IT DOWN AND SEEING IF IT WAS SOME KIND OF MONITOR RYKER'S BEEN USING ON ME?

PRESENTLY TRACING AUDIT TRAIL TO LOCATE SOURCE AND NULLIFY.

FINE, MEANTIME I FEEL LIKE A PIECE OF LAUNDRY LEFT OUT TO DRY...

IF I HAD MEMORY TAPES I COULD TAKE CARE OF THAT CREEPY FEELING I ALWAYS HAVE OF BEING PERSECUTED BY EVERYONE. IF THIS IS WHAT IT'S LIKE TO FEEL LIKE THE GOD MACHINE RYKER SET OUT TO MAKE ME -- FORGET IT!

UH...THAT FIGHT TOOK MORE OUTTA ME 'N I THOUGHT. PLOT A COURSE...

ESCAPE ROUTE OFFERS INNUMERABLE POSSIBILITES ALGORITHMS DICTATE--

JUST GET US OUTTA HERE, WILL YA? JUST USE THE CO-ORDINATES I JUST PUNCHED.

C'MON. LET'S LIFT.

PRESENT COURSE TAKING US 57.4 MILES FROM MANHATTAN, OVER STATE OF NEW JERSEY--

GUESS I DIDN'T KNOW WHAT I WAS DOIN' WHEN I PUNCHED THAT CODE.

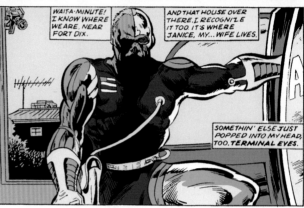

WAIT-A-MINUTE! I KNOW WHERE WE ARE, NEAR FORT DIX.

AND THAT HOUSE OVER THERE, I RECOGNIZE IT TOO. IT'S WHERE JANICE, MY...WIFE LIVES.

SOMETHIN' ELSE JUST POPPED INTO MY HEAD, TOO. TERMINAL EYES.

REMEMBER, 'PUTER? TERMINAL EYES? "COMPLITER EYES RECORDING EVERYTHING!"

BET RYKER'S GOT THE WHOLE AREA STAKED OUT WITH CAMERAS.

WATCHIN' ME, PROBLY KNOWING I WAS GONNA COME HERE, EVEN THOUGH I DIDN'T EVEN KNOW IT

WARNING: SYSTEMS OPERATING UNDER CRIPPLE MODE.

YOU SAID THAT BEFORE. YOU WORRY TOO MUCH, 'PUTER. I'LL MAKE IT...

GOT TO. I WANNA SEE JANIS AGAIN.

...EXPLAIN TO HER.

EVERYTHING'LL BE OKAY--

WHEN I GET MY STRENGTH BACK, I'LL MAKE EVERYTHING ALL RIGHT.

MIKE, MIKE, IS THAT YOU--?

I'VE BEEN SO *WORRIED*. MAJOR RYKER HASN'T CALLED FOR DAYS...

I'M... I'M GOING OUT OF MY MIND WITH WORRY!

I'M SO GLAD YOU...,

JANICE.

OH...

JANICE, IT'S ME, *LUTHER*, YOUR *HUSBAND!*

I CAN'T EXPLAIN IT ALL NOW-- HOW I GOT THIS WAY-- BUT...

Y-YOU'RE SOME KIND OF HIDEOUS *MONSTER!!*

GET... *AWAY... FROM...* ME!!

NO, YOU'VE GOT IT ALL WRONG IT'S *ME*, JANICE-- DON'T YOU RECOGNIZE MY *VOICE?*

DON'T START SCREAM- ING, PLEASE! I'VE COME BACK TO TAKE CARE OF YOU, I--

SUBJECT NEARING HYSTERICS SUBJECT IS NOT A TARGET, THERE CAN BE NO LOGICAL REASON FOR REMAINING. SUGGESTED COURSE --

YOU'RE RIGHT, SHE'S BREAKING DOWN. AND MAYBE I WAS WRONG TO COME IN HERE, LET HER SEE ME LIKE *THIS*--

BUT SOMEHOW I'VE *GOT* TO CONVINCE HER I'M *ALIVE!* THAT LUTHER MANNING *DID NOT DIE!* I'VE GOT TO!

MOMMY...

MOMMY?

OH NO! NO! NOT MY BABY!

A LITTLE BOY. MY LITTLE BOY, JANICE WAS PREGNANT WITH HIM--

--AND I NEVER GOT TO SEE HIM!

NO... PLEASE...

NOT... MY... BABY...

HOW OLD WOULD HE BE? FOUR? FIVE?

I'VE GOT TO SEE HIM! MY BOY!

IF IT WEREN'T FOR RYKER, I COULD HAVE BEEN A FATHER TO HIM.

COULD HAVE TAUGHT HIM TO WALK...TO TALK.

PLEASE! PLEASE DON'T HURT HIM...? PLEASE...?

OH GOD, NO!

I CAN'T GO IN THERE. NOT LIKE THIS!

I COULDN'T BEAR HIS REJECTION, TOO!

YOU DON'T BELONG IN MY BODY, BUT I PUT UP WITH YOU.

WARNING: PRESENT ACTIONS ILLOGICAL AND CONTRARY TO...

..CONTRARY TO WHAT? YOU'RE THE THING THAT'S CONTRARY, 'PUTER.

AND YOU CAN'T TELL ME WHAT TO FEEL!

I'VE HAD IT...WITH A *MACHINE* TALKING A LOT OF BUNK IN MY *HEAD* WHEN I'M TRYING TO *SALVAGE* WHAT'S LEFT OF MY *LIFE*.

I WOULD HAVE BEEN BETTER OFF *DYING* AT WAR-WOLF'S HANDS!

WHAT'S THE MATTER,'PUTER? NO ANSWERS? NO *TELLING* ME WHAT TO DO--PROGRAMMING MY EVERY ACTION?

TELL ME WHAT TO DO NOW,'PUTER!

TELL ME,'PUTER, TELL ME!

WHAT...

..IS...

..THERE...

LEFT?

CLICK!

FUNCTION OF LASER HAS BEEN TERMINATED BECAUSE ACTION IS CONTRARY TO PROGRAMMING.

SUICIDE NOT PROGRAMMED, NO ALGORITHMS ANALOGOUS TO SELF-DESTRUCTION.

I CAN'T EVEN *CHOOSE* MY WAY OF DYING. CAN'T *KILL* MYSELF. CAN'T *LIVE*. NOWHERE TO GO...

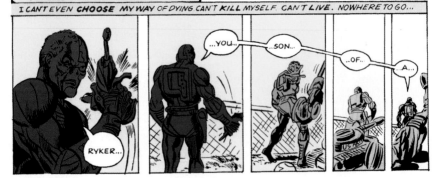

...YOU...

...SON...

..OF..

..A...

RYKER...

[60]

PROLOGUE: Go on, Luther Manning. Pound your armored fist against the earth in frustrated rage. You have good reason to. For where once you shared your life with a wife and child, now you share your "life" with a machine. Where once you were a man of flesh and blood, now you are only a cyborg, a half-human mechanism programmed solely for destruction...yet unable to destroy YOURSELF!

STan Lee PRESENTS: **DEATHLOK** THE DEMOLISHER

Five to One, DEATHLOK...

...One in Five...

CONCEPT, SCRIPT & ARTWORK: RICH BUCKLER | LETTERING: KAREN POCOCK COLORING: L. LESSMANN | EDITOR: LEN WEIN | INSPIRATION AND ENCOURAGEMENT: JUST ABOUT THE WHOLE BLAMED BULLPEN!

LUCKY IF EVEN ONE FLAKING BUILDING IS STILL **STANDING!**

WHAT IN BLAZES HAPPENED HERE?

WHAT--?

I JUST CAN'T **BELIEVE** I COULD HAVE WALKED AROUND IN THIS **RUBBLE**--

READ-OUT: HELICOPTER ON AUTOMATIC STAND-BY ALERT.

SO--? A LITTLE **WALKING** AIN'T GONNA HURT US.

EXTRAPOLATION: POSSIBILITY OF THREATS WITHIN THE MIDTOWN PERIPHERY 63.00017%...

I CAN'T **BELIEVE** IT...

ALL THE PLACES **JANICE** --MY WIFE -- AND I WENT TO WHEN I WAS--

--**NORMAL!** ALL OF IT... **GONE!** THE RESTAURANTS, THEATERS... EVERYTHING THAT WAS PRECIOUS TO ME... GONE.

TERMINAL EYE: LOCKED IN ON MONITOR X-14838--

--SUBJECT DEATHLOK LOCATED AT FOLLOWING CO-ORDINATES

YOU MADE IT MORE **DIFFICULT** FOR ME WHEN YOU LOCATED MY **COMPUTER** "**BUG**" INSIDE YOU, DEATHLOK--

--NOW I CAN'T RECORD THE **ECSTATIC SYNAPTIC** SENSATIONS OF YOUR VIOLENCE!

BUT NO MATTER--

--ENJOY YOUR **FREEDOM** WHILE YOU STILL **HAVE** IT, DEATHLOK!

IT'S NOT A **DEATH-MACHINE** THE WORLD NEEDS NOW-- OR AN **ARMY** OF WALKING **DEATH-SOLDIERS**, AS I HAD ONCE ENVISIONED--

--BUT A **SAVIOUR MACHINE!**

PITY YOU CAN'T *HEAR* ME, DEATHLOK.

IN FACT--

--EVERY-THING I DO IS PERFORMED IN ABSOLUTE *SECRECY*--

"--WHILE YOUR *EVERY MOVE* IS RECORDED VIA MY *OMNI-COMPUTER!*"

US ARMY

"*I'VE* KNOWN *EVERY-THING* YOU'VE DONE.

"... EVEN AFTER YOU ESCAPED MY *CYBORG* WAR-WOLF IN THE STA-TUE OF *LIBERTY* AND FLED TO THE HOME OF YOUR-- SHALL WE SAY-- *EX-WIFE.* DID YOU *REALLY* BELIEVE SHE WOULD *GREET* YOU--

"...WITH ANYTHING BUT *REVULSION?* YOU, A MONSTER, A WALK-ING PATCHWORK OF *FLESH* AND *WIRES*... NO LONGER HER *HUSBAND.*

"*YOU REALIZED* THIS EVEN IN YOUR WEAKENED, BATTLE-STRICKEN STATE--

"--AND FLED YOUR 'HOME' BEFORE EVEN *SEEING* YOUR FIVE-YEAR-OLD SON!"

"*YOU* SOUGHT, IN DESPERATION, THE ONLY WAY *OUT* YOU THOUGHT WAS LEFT--

"-- BUT THE COM-PUTER INSIDE YOU...

"PREDICTABLY--

"--DENIED YOU EVEN *THAT* SOLUTION.

"SO YOU DESTROYED YOUR *THREE-THOUSAND DOLLAR LASER-WEAPON.*

"*TEMPER, TEMPER.*

"*CONTRARY* TO YOUR *PRIME DIRECTIVE,* YOU KNOW. *MY* DIREC-TIVE, DEATHLOK! I WOULDN'T *LET* YOU KILL YOURSELF!"

OF COURSE *NOT!* IT WOULD BE TOO EASY! A MAN *LOCKED IN DEATH*...

... SHOULD NOT BE AL-LOWED TO KILL HIMSELF!

WHY, THAT WOULD BE *CHEAT-ING!*

NO, NOT WHEN HIS *MASTER* CAN ACCOMPLISH THE TASK--

--IN, SHALL WE SAY-- A MORE *COLOR-FUL MANNER?* HAH, HAH!

YES, SLEEP YOUR *ELECTRIC SLEEP*, MY SWEET *NINA!*

IT REALLY *WAS UNFORTUNATE* THAT YOU SAW ME DAYS AGO...

...WHEN I WAS RECHARGING MY *BIO-FEEDBACK MECHANISM!*

NOW, YOU *TOO* HAVE BECOME MY PRISON-ER, ALONG WITH *MIKE TRAVERS!*

BUT I *CARED* ABOUT *YOU...* BEFORE...

YOU MUST *UNDERSTAND*, MY LOVE, THAT I CAN'T LEAVE YOU RUNNING AROUND *FREE...*

...TO TELL *EVERYONE...* THAT *I*, TOO, AM A *CYBORG.*

I COULDN'T TAKE THE CHANCE OF YOU *FIND-ING* OUT--

THAT UNLIKE *DEATHLOK--I* WAS *PROJECT ALPHA-MECH'S* FIRST FAILURE!

TERMINAL EYE: DEATHLOK WITHIN MID-TOWN WALL...

...APPROXI-MATELY TEN KILOMETERS FROM PERIPHERY OF *BLACK MARKET MEAT OPERATION...*

ALERT! POSSIBLE TAR-GETS NEARBY. ANALY-SIS: HUMANOID CANNIBALS. DISPLAYING SIGNS OF FEAR--

YEAH, I *KNOW.*

I CAN *SMELL* THE FEAR IN 'EM FROM *HERE.*

Y'KNOW, I JUST HAD A *HORRIBLE THOUGHT.* WHAT IF ALL THAT BLACK MARKET *MEAT* BACK THERE WAS...*HUMAN?*

89.937% POSSIBILITY.

THAT'S A PRETTY *STRONG* POSSIBILITY.

AFFIRMATIVE.

TERMINAL EYE: DEATH-LOK CYBORG HAS EN-TERED 42ND STREET LIBRARY/MUSEUM...

SLIMY RATS. THEY HAVEN'T GOT THE GUTS TO COME OUT IN THE OPEN!

HEY, THEY COULD BE RYKER'S MEN-- LIKE THE LAST TIME WHEN ONE OF 'EM TOOK A BITE OUTTA MY KNEE! A FEW OF THEM FOR A DIVERSION-- MAYBE ALL OF 'EM SOMEHOW UN-DER RYKER'S CONTROL!

SAY WHAT HAVE WE HERE? GRAFFITI?

AFFIRMATIVE.

NO ONE HERE GETS OUT ALIVE! THEY'VE GOT THE GUNS

SOME KIND OF REVOLU-TION

MUST'VE OCCUR-RED WHILE I WAS FROZEN...

BUT WE'VE GOT THE NUMBERS!

GONNA WIN, WE'RE TAKING OVER!

...WAITING TO BE "RESUR-RECTED" BY RYKER'S BUTCHERS!

SEEMS LIKE A LOT CAN HAPPEN IN FIVE YEARS, 'PUTER.

A LOT!

IF RYKER'S CON-TROLLING NEW YORK-

THEN IT'S NOT UN-LIKELY HE'S INTO MUCH MORE! I DON'T KNOW HOW, BUT--

WHAT'S THIS?

HAVEN'T SEEN A REAL BOOK SINCE HOLOGRAPHS RE-PLACED THE OLD METHODS OF STORING--

-- KNOWLEDGE...

FRANKENSTEIN BY MARY SHELLEY

FRANK

TERMINAL EYE: DEATHLOK CYBORG UNAWARE OF CANNIBAL-DECOYS. INITIATING PHASE TWO OF PLAN.

DEATHMAN...

CHAPTER TWO

That BOOK has given me a few ideas, 'PUTER-- like, if RYKER had SURGEONS to put ME TOGETHER--

--NOW, FIVE YEARS LATER, there MUST be a GUY out there who can HELP me-- SOMEHOW-- if the PRICE is right.

AFFIRMATIVE, THERE WERE THREE SURGEONS WHO PERFORMED THE OPERATION.

WERE?

CORRECT: TWO OF THEM WERE ELIMINATED AS TARGETS OF JULIAN BRIGGS, ILLEGAL RACKETEER.

--AND IT WAS ME THAT DID THE ELIMINATING.

OUTMANEUVERED BY RYKER AGAIN.

YOU SAID "THREE": WHAT ABOUT A THIRD?

NOT SUFFICIENT DATA TO EXTRAPOLATE.

THEN I'LL HAVE TO FIND HIM--BY TURNING THIS CRUM-MY CITY IN-SIDE OUT!

IT'S RYKER, TRYING TO SET ME UP AGAIN. BUT FOR WHAT?

ALERT: SUBJECTS POTENTIALLY DANGEROUS, BUT NOT TARGETS.

I THOUGHT YOU GUYS HAD THE FIGHT KNOCKED OUTTA YA--

--THE LAST TIME WE MET UP!*

*WAY BACK IN DEATH-LOK'S PREMIERE ISSUE ASTONISHING TALES #25. --LEN

YOU MEAN RUN. RUN AWAY FROM THESE SNIVELING ANIMALS? NO WAY!!

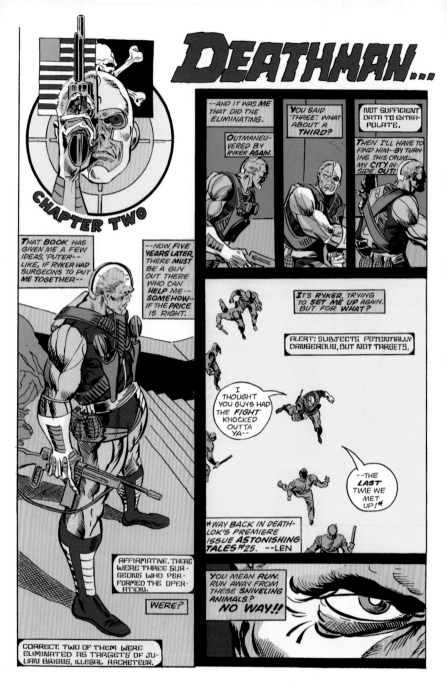

FOLLOW ME NO MORE!

I JUST HEARD A NOISE. WE'RE BEING *FOLLOWED.*

CORRECT.

SENSORS INDICATE PRESENCE OF SIX CANNIBALS.

I CAN TAKE 'EM OUT *WITHOUT* ARTILLERY.

BUT WHY DID THEY WAIT UNTIL NOW BEFORE ATTACKING?

WHY *THIS* PLACE, AT *THIS* PARTICULAR *TIME?*

ANOMALY! PRESENT ACTION UNWARRANTED. SUBJECTS ARE *NOT* TARGETS.

WHOSE SIDE ARE YOU *ON?* THEY'RE LOOKING AT ME LIKE I'M THE *MORNING MENU!*

REPEAT: SUBJECTS ARE *NOT* TARGETS. TAKE EVASIVE ACTION.

I'VE BEEN *PROGRAMMED FOR DESTRUCTION*--SO WHY NOT *ENJOY A LITTLE OF IT?*

NOT PROGRAMMED FOR EMOTION. ALL UNITS WILL RESPOND *ONLY*--

FROM *NOW* ON I RESPOND, TO ONLY ONE THING, 'PUTER. MY *HUMAN* INSTINCT FOR *SURVIVAL.* PERIOD!

--FOUR.

--ONE CANNIBAL--

--TWO CANNIBALS--

--THREE CANNIBALS--

OWWIE.

THIS IS ALMOST TOO EASY!

--NUMBER SIX LEAVES NO MORE!

--AND--

AH, AH-- NOW THAT WASN'T NICE!

I TAKE THIS ONE OUT --

AND THE ENEMY IS--

--US!

DETECT SOMETHING CLOSER. HOMING IN ON ENEMY.

I CAN SEE-- EVEN IF ONE OF MY EYES IS AN INFRARED SCOPTIC LENS!

SENSORS INDICATE MOVEMENT OF HEAVY VEHICLE THIRTY FEET.

I KNOW WHERE IT IS!

--THAT?

WELL, 'PUTER...

GUESS THAT TAKES CARE OF--

IT'S A TANK! A FREAKIN' TANK!!

THAT ANSWERS ONE NAGGING QUESTION. HOW MUCH RYKER **MEANT** WHEN HE THREATENED ME!

IF HE WANTS ME **THIS BAD--**

-- THEN IT'S A SURE THING HE **DOESN'T** WANT ME IN ONE PIECE!

-- MECHANISM MAY FAIL TO IGNITE.

-- REMOTE POSSI-BILITY EXISTS THAT--

SUGGESTION NOTED. HOWEVER, DUE TO AGE OF WEAPONRY AND ADDED UN-KNOWN FACTORS--

DANGER INHERENT; MECHANISM USED AS MISSILE IS ANTI-QUATED.

SOMETIMES THE OLD-FASHIONED WAYS ARE **BEST**, 'PUTER.

ALERT!

THAT THING HAS ENOUGH POWER TO SPREAD ME ALL OVER MANHATTAN!

AND IT'LL DO IT--

--UNLESS--

IF THOSE "BABIES" WERE *LIVE* IT WOULD *DEFINITELY* HAVE SPOILED MY DAY!

WARNING: UNDER FIRE. POTENTIAL TARGETS LEAVING VEHICLE.

RYKER AIN'T PULLING ANY *PUNCHES!*

THOSE CREEPS ARE PACKING *LASERS* WITH HEAT CONVERSION UNITS!

I'D BETTER HAUL MY PROSTHETIC TAIL *OUTTA HERE--*

--WHILE I'VE STILL *GOT* ONE!

A FEW SHORT HOURS AGO--

--I *WANTED* TO DIE! NOW I'M NOT SO CONVINCED--

-- IT WAS SUCH A *HOT IDEA!*

OKAY, BABES-- JUST HOLD IT *RIGHT THERE!*

DANGER IMMINENT.

TERMINAL EYE: OMNI-READ-OUT ON OBSERVATION CELL FOR CAPTIVE *LIEUTENANT MIKE TRAVERS:*

RYKER, I DON'T KNOW IF YOU'RE LISTENING, BUT...

...YOU'RE NOT *KEEPING* ME IN THIS GILDED CAGE FOR LONG.

SUBJECT IS PUNCHING OUT STANDARD CODE. DOES NOT APPEAR TO BE PLEASED--

THIS FOOD *TASTES* LIKE IT WAS MADE BY A *MACHINE!* PTOOH!

SUBJECT IN AGITATED STATE--RESTLESS, HEARTBEAT IRREGULAR. PROGNOSIS: ANGER AND FRUSTRATION.

YOU'RE WELCOME TO TAG *ALONG*--

--IF YOU WANNA BE THERE TO PICK UP *WHAT'S LEFT OF ME!*

OMNI-COMPUTER DATA REPORT: DEATHLOK HAS TEMPORARILY ELUDED **TROUBLE-SHOOTERS**. TANK-CAR IS NOW HOMING IN ON CYBORG. HEAT SENSORS, HOWEVER, INDICATE PRESENCE OF **ADDITIONAL TARGET**.

TERMINAL EYE: MONITOR CONFIRMS REPORT.

HEY!

HEY, *WAITAMINIT!*

I'M COMING ALONG!

CANNIBAL DECOYS HAVE LURED DEATHLOK TO THE **NORTHERN WALL**.

GOOD, GOOD! *EXCELLENT!* NOW MY DEAR *NINA*, WE WILL MAKE FULL USE OF *YOUR BRAIN!*

EVEN NOW YOUR BRAIN'S *IMPULSES* ARE BEING MONITORED AND CODED--

--WITH YOUR MIND FUNCTIONING IN RAPPORT WITH MY *OMNI-COMPUTER*, THE RESULTING EFFECT IS A *THINKING*, ALMOST *HUMAN* TANK-WEAPON!

A FORMIDABLE WEAPON, INDEED. AND IF MEN ARMED WITH *LASERS* DO NOT GET TO HIM *FIRST*--

--MY *SUPER-TANK* WILL!

I'LL SCATTER DEATHLOK INTO A *MILLION* SHREDS THAT NO SURGEON COULD *EVER* REASSEMBLE!

LOGICAL COURSE OF ACTION: PROCEED TO HELICOPTER.

LOCATION: TWO BLOCKS EAST.

GOOD IDEA, 'PUTER. GLAD I THOUGHT OF IT!

OKAY, LET'S GO *THIS WAY.* MY 'COPTER IS ONLY A BLOCK AWAY FROM HERE...

YOU'VE GOT A 'COPTER? A HELICOPTER!

WARNING: RYKER'S SURROGATES IN VICINITY OF COPTER--

RYKER.

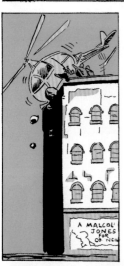

A MALCOL' JONES FOR CO'NCIL

CORRECTION...

...I *HAD* A 'COPTER!

WHAT MADE YOU WANNA FOLLOW *ME,* ANYWAY, PAL?

THE GRAPEVINE HAS IT THAT THERE'S A NEW *SAVIOUR MACHINE* BUILT BY RYKER!

WE-- THE PEOPLE SUP- PORTING THE *REBELLION AGAINST RYKER--*

--WE FIGURE YOU'RE IT!

THAT'S A *GOOD* ONE!

YOU THINK I'M SOME *NEW MESSIAH!* ME--

--A *BORN LOSER!!*

FURTHER MOVEMENT IM- POSSIBLE DUE TO BARRIER.

IT'S THE *NORTHERN WALL!*

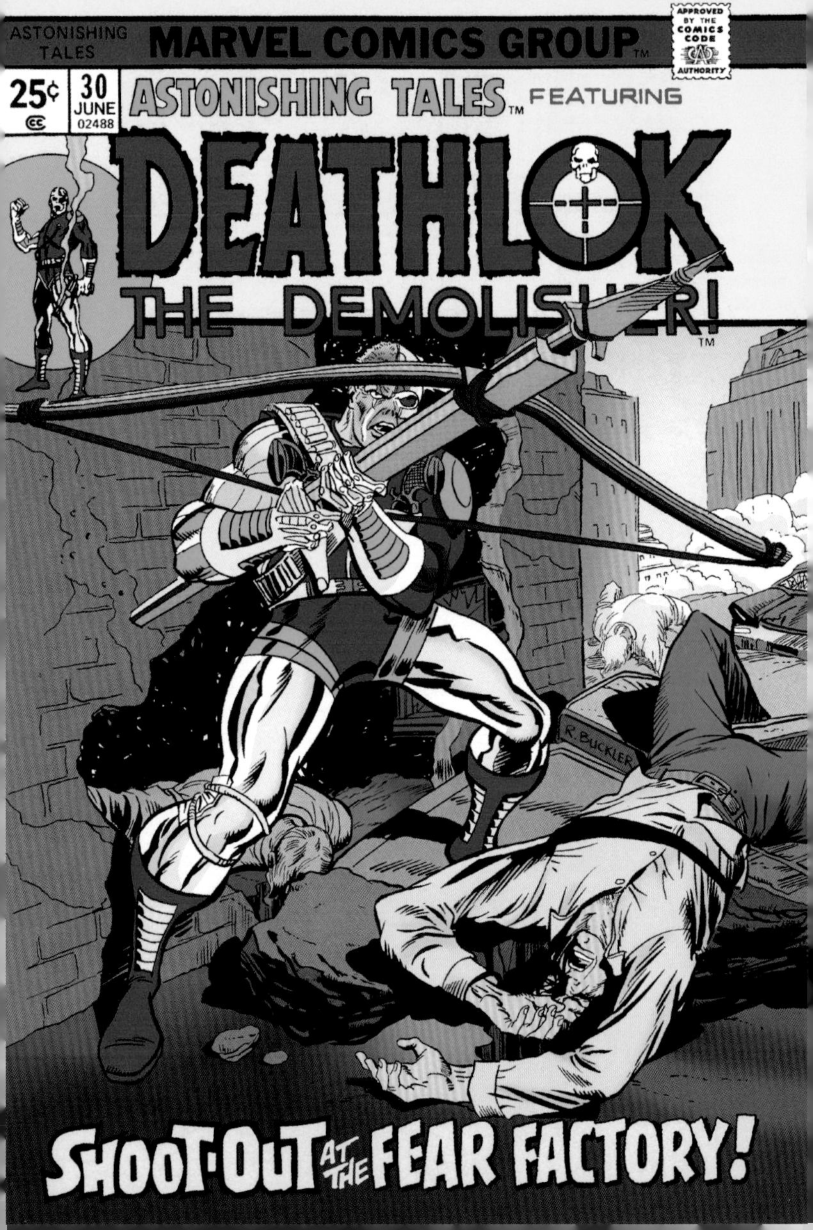
ASTONISHING TALES
MARVEL COMICS GROUP TM
APPROVED BY THE COMICS CODE AUTHORITY
25¢
30 JUNE 02488
ASTONISHING TALES TM FEATURING
DEATHLOK THE DEMOLISHER! TM
R. BUCKLER
SHOOT-OUT AT THE FEAR FACTORY!

STAN LEE PRESENTS: **DEATHLOK** THE **DEMOLISHER**™

THE SOFT PARADE...

READ OUT: TANK-CAR ANTIQUE IN NATURE. ALL SYSTEMS MODGRNIZGD, HOWEVER. DANGER IMMINENT.

...OF SLOW, SLIDING DEATH!

RICH BUCKLER
PLOT/LAYOUTS
SCRIPT (PG. 1-3)

DOUG MOENCH
SCRIPT (PG. 6-32)

ART:
RICH BUCKLER
KEITH POLLARD
ARVELL JONES

AL McWILLIAMS,
INKING

G. ROUSSOS,
COLORIST

C. JETTER-
LETTERING

LEN WEIN,
EDITOR

MY GUN!

IT'S JAMMED! AND THAT TANK IS GETTING READY TO FIRE!

BARRIER BEHIND HAS ESTIMATED THICKNESS OF THREE FEET. RETREAT IS IMPOSSIBLE.

GRAB SOME COVER QUICK, SOLDIER, 'CUZ--

HEY, WHERE THE DEVIL DO YOU THINK YOU'RE-- GOING?

TO FIGHT ME A WAR, BABY--!

WARNING: DEATH MACHINE'S FIRING MECHANISM LOCKED INTO POSITION, PREPARING TO--

--FIRE!

UH-UH--

I ALREADY GAVE *MY* LIFE FOR MY COUNTRY--

--ANOTHER MARTYR WE DON'T *NEED!*

READ-OUT: MULTIPLE PUNCTURE WOUNDS CAUSED BY SHRAPNEL. CRIPPLE-MODE CONDITIONS--

YOU GOT A *ONE-EQUALS-ONE* KINDA THINKING, 'PUTER. GOT IT ALL BROKEN DOWN TA *LOGIC*, HUH?

LUTH'-- LOOK OUT!

OOF!

JUST--

--MISSED THAT 'CUSSION BOMB!

SO WHY DO I KEEP HAVING *MENTAL BACKLASHES*--

--TO WHEN I WAS *LUTHER MANNING*--WHEN MIKE TRAVERS HAD *SAVED* MY *LIFE*--?

MEMORY SYNAPSE DELAY.

IS THAT WHATCHA CALL IT? WELL, WHICH IS MORE *REAL*, 'PUTER? THE STUFF IN MY HEAD THAT KEEPS *REPLAYING* LIKE A *TAPE-LOOP*--?

--OR THE REALITY OF THIS *WAKING MOMENT*?

TELL ME 'PUTER. WHICH ONE?

QUESTION IRRELEVANT.

TANK-CAR IN POSITION TO FIRE AGAIN AT POINT BLANK RANGE. TARGET: US.

YIPE! SUDDENLY IT ALL COMES BACK TO ME!

RYKER'S HOLDING OFF--

--TOYING WITH ME, WAITING FOR... *SOMETHING*. WHAT?

{UNNNNN...}

--EVEN IF WE HAVE TO BREAK MY STINKIN' *SWIVEL-SOCKET* BALL-JOINTS TO DO IT!

BURN 'IM--'CAUSE IF HE GETS OVER THAT *WALL*, RYKER'LL BURN *US*!

WARNING: ANCILLARY WEIGHT IMPEDES MOMENTUM AND TRAJECTORY OF JUMP. JETTISON EXTRANEOUS BURDEN OR SUFFER FAILURE PROJECTED AS ULTIMATE DEACTIVATION.

NO WAY, 'PUTER! EITHER THIS DUDE GOES OVER *WITH* ME--OR WE *BOTH* FRY!

HANG ON, BUSTER--THE REVOLUTION AIN'T OVER *YET!*

YOU--*MADE* IT--!

I NEVER WOULDA THOUGHT IT *POSSIBLE.* MAYBE YOU AIN'T THE *SAVIOR MACHINE,* BUT LINC SHANE *KNOWS* WHEN HE'S BEEN *SAVED*--

--AND TO ME, BABY, YOU ARE THE *SAVIN'EST* MACHINE I *EVER* DID--

--*UHHUN!!*

NO!!

STATUS REPORT: LIFE FUNCTIONS TERMINATED IN SUBJECT NOW IDENTIFIED AS LINC SHANE.

NO. *WHY?!*

WHAT DID HE DIE FOR--?!

JETTISON UNNECESSARY BURDEN.

REPEAT: JETTISON CORPSE AND EXECUTE EVASIVE ACTION. DANGER REMAINS EXTANT.

A WASTE-- HIS DEATH WAS A SENSELESS WASTE--!

HE STOOD UP TO RYKER'S GOONS ON HIS OWN--ALL ALONE... AND FOR WHAT?!

REPEAT: SITUATION DICTATES FLIGHT.

JUST SO HE COULD LEAVE A SHRED OF MOTH-EATEN, GAUDY CLOTH BEHIND HIM--? IS THIS WHAT HE DIED FOR--?!

REPEAT: DANGER, DANGER, DANGER.

ALL RIGHT, 'PUTER! CAN'T A MAN EVEN THINK FOR A SECOND?

TEAM "MAN" DOES NOT COMPUTE.

SHUT UP AND GIVE ME A READOUT ON THAT SMALLER WALL AHEAD.

COLUMBUS CIRCLE PERIMETER OF BARRICADE SURROUNDING CENTRAL PARK; PRESENT SOBRIQUET, "SUICIDE PARK."

MIGHT AS WELL HOP IT THEN. BEEN WANTIN' TO COMMIT--

HUH--?!

THE CLANKING--!

IT'S THAT STINKIN' TANK AGAIN!!

CORRECT.

SUBJECT VEHICLE APPROACHING AT VELOCITY SUFFICIENT TO...

...PENETRATE ALREADY DAMAGED WALL.

YA DON'T SAY, BRIGHT-BRAIN.

LOOKS LIKE SUICIDE IS PARKIN' ITSELF ON BOTH SIDES OF THIS WALL --'CUZ IF I STAY ON THIS SIDE...

...I'M JUST ASKIN' TO BUY IT--!

CONCLUSION CORRECT--

ALTHOUGH TERMINOLOGY IS SPECIOUS, ANTI-QUATED, CONTEXTUALLY EMOTIONAL, AND INIMICAL TO INTRINSIC NATURE OF CYBER-NETIC ORGANISM. FURTHERMORE...

FURTHERMORE, STUFF IT UP YOUR TRANSIS-TORIZED NOSE BEFORE YOUR POMPOUS YAMMERIN' MAKES ME--

UHNN--!!

--CRACKED MY LEAD-PLATED SKULL GREAT... JUST GREAT...

OMNI-COMPUTER TERMINAL EYE READOUT ON SUBJECT MIKE TRAVERS: ALTHOUGH INCARCERATED WITHIN TERMINAL NODE-HOUSING PROGRAMMED FOR COMPLETE SOLITUDE AND SYCOPHANTIC PROVISION, SUBJECT REMAINS AGITATED. INCREASING DISSATISFACTION, RESENTMENT, RESTLESSNESS AND CLAUSTROPHOBIA. EXTRAPOLATION: ALL TENDANCY-LOCK EVALUATIONS INDICATE SUBJECT WILL ATTEMPT ESCAPE AT ALL COST. WARNING.

I KNOW YOUR COMPUTER IS *SPY-ING* ON ME, RYKER...

...AND I'LL JUST BET YOU *LOVE* PLAYIN' ZOO-KEEPER!

BUT THIS IS *ONE* MONKEY WHO AIN'T PUTTIN' ON ANY *SHOWS* FOR GAWK-ERS LIKE *YOU*--!

AND THIS IS *ONE* MONKEY WHO'S GONNA *TURN THE TRICK* ON HIS *KEEPER*-- SO KEEP YOUR EYES GLUED TO THE *MONITOR*, RYKER.

I AIN'T WARNIN' YA *AGAIN*.

EXCELLENT... *EXCELLENT*. THE DEATHLOK CYBORG IS RUNNING *SCARED* NOW. IN LESS THAN *MINUTES*, MY SUPREME *DEATH-MACHINE* WILL OVERTAKE AND *EXPUNGE* HIM...

...PROVING THAT EVEN A BRILLIANT *MILITARY STRATEGIST* LIKE *LUTHER MANNING* IS NO MORE THAN A PETTY *ANNOY-ANCE* TO MY *SUPERIOR INTELLECT*--!

WAIT A MINUTE--! HE'S VAULTING THE WALL INTO THE *PARK*. HE'S GOING TO--

NO. HE'S *TUMBLED*-- INJURED HIS HEAD...

GOOD. IT'LL GIVE THE *DEATH-MACHINE TANK* TIME TO BREACH THE WALL AND *FINISH* HIM...

OMNI-COMPUTER. I WANT AN *AUDIO READOUT NARRATIVE*--NOW.

TERMINAL EYE: SUBJECT DEATHLOK CYBORG SUFFERING SYNAPSE DISORIENTATION. MOMENTARILY INOPER-ATIVE. HOWEVER, CHEMO-SOLUTION SIMULATING ORGANIC ADRENALIN NOW RUSHING TO HIS BRAIN. SUBJECT REGAINING FULL CONTROL OF FACULTIES. EXPERIENCING ANOMALOUS EMOTIONAL IMPETUS TO SURVIVE.

STILL *DAZED*...

...BUT IF I DON'T PULL A *JACK-IN-THE-BOX* NUMBER...

..AND SPLIT BUT *FAST*...

...THIS IS GONNA BE THE *LAST DAY*...

...I'M *EVER* DAZED--!

TERMINAL EYE: PROGRESS OF DEATH-MACHINE MOMENT-ARILY OBSTRUCTED BY WALL. NOW INITIATING COMPENSATE-FACTOR.

--'CAUSE IF WE DON'T TAKE SOME *ON-FOOT* INITIATIVE...

...RYKER'S GONNA GIVE OUR *LASERS*-- AND OUR RIGHT TO *LIVE*--TO A *NEW* CREW OF TROUBLE-SHOOTERS!

STATISTICAL PROJECTION: PURSUING VEHICLE LOGS 99.898% PROBABILITY OF REACHING WALL. ADDITIONALLY, FIVE HUMAN SUBJECTS NOW EXECUTING AMBULANT PURSUIT.

THANKS, 'PUTER. CHEER ME UP, WHY DON'T YA?

EITHER I GET *BLASTED* FROM HERE TO *GUTSVILLE* BY THE *TANK*--OR SLASHED TO BRIGHT RED RIBBONS BY THE LASERS THOSE FIVE *BOZOS* ARE LUGGIN'--!

THE TANK'S *BACKIN' UP* FOR SPEED TO PLOW THROUGH THE *WALL*...

BUT WE AIN'T GOT TIME TO *WAIT*--!

I AIN'T HAD SO MUCH *FUN* SINCE MY *BLOOD* WAS *PICKLED* AND SUBSTITUTED WITH *BATTERY ACID*.

GIMME THE DOPE ON THIS SHACK---AND WITHOUT ANY OF YOUR BULL--!

FORMERLY AN AUXILIARY WEAPONS ARMORY; NOW ABANDONED.

WEAPONS, HUH? AND THESE BARS WANNA KEEP ME AWAY FROM 'EM...

BUT NO SUNLIGHT-SLICIN' MOTHER-CAGIN' BARS --

--ARE EVER GONNA KEEP ME IN OR OUT OF ANYTHING AGAIN--!

NOW...

... ABOUT THOSE WEAPONS...

GRENADES...

OUTMODED AND OBSOLETE NATURE PROHIBITS...

YEAH, YEAH...I REMEMBER HOW THEY DUDDED-OUT LAST TIME I TRIED 'EM, BUT MAYBE THESE ARE--

THAT SCUFFLIN'!. FOOTSTEPS.. ...AT LEAST TWO SETS...

AFFIRMATIVE; TWO HUMAN ANTAGONISTS APPROACHING EAST WALL OF ARMORY.

NATURE: FURTIVE.

SHHHH!

NEVER HEARD A LOUDER SHUSH IN ALL MY DEATH--!

ALL RIGHT, GET READY FOR--

AGH-K!

HOLY SON OF A--

FIRST SUBJECT SUCCESSFULLY EXTIRPATED.

YEAH, AND *NOW* IT'S TIME TO DRAG OUT MY *TWO-GUN KID-CORPSE* ROUTINE...

SORTA WISH I HADN'T FISTED MY *LASER PISTOL* INTO SLAG---BUT THAT'S *LIFE*, I GUESS...

...OR AT LEAST *DEATH*.

HEY, *CREAMPUFF*--! WHAT'S THE *RUSH*?

LOST YOUR *TASTE* FOR *WASTIN*'--?

I HAVEN'T!

SECOND SUBJECT SUCCESSFULLY EXTIRPATED.

Y'KNOW, 'PUTER, THESE OLD *PEA-SHOOTERS* ARE KINDA FUN...PACK A LITTLE *RECOIL-KICK* YOU DON'T FIND IN A *LASER*...

WARNING: DANGER IMMINENT. REMAINING THREE PURSUANTS ENCROACHING RAPIDLY. FLIGHT MANDATED.

THE MORE THE MERRIER, I GUESS...JUST WISH I HAD TIME TO SNATCH THIS CREAMPUFF'S *LASER-RIFLE*--RECOIL-KICK OR *NOT*...

SHOOTOUT at the FLESH FACTORY!

WHAT'S THE JOINT UP AHEAD, 'PUTER?

A DEFUNCT CRYOGENICS INSTALLATION.

Y'MEAN WHERE THEY PUT STIFFS ON *ICE*-- FREEZE 'EM--AND THAW 'EM BACK TO LIFE *LATER*?

AFFIRMATIVE. THIS PARTICULAR INSTALLATION ALSO FUNCTIONED AS A MEDICAL FACILITY WHERE ILLEGAL SURGERY WAS ALLEGEDLY PERFORMED.

ILLEGAL SURGERY...YOU MEAN LIKE ME--CYBORGS AND STUFF?

PRECISELY.

JUST HOW MANY CYBORGS ARE THERE RUNNIN' AROUND--?

INSUFFICIENT DATA. DOES NOT COMPUTE.

FIGURES--RYKER CLOAKS HIMSELF IN SECRECY THE WAY THAT STINKIN' TANK CLOAKS ITSELF WITH ARMOR...

SAY...I SEEM TO REMEMBER THIS SITE...

THE SANITATION DEPARTMENT USED IT AT ONE TIME...STASHED GARBAGE IN THERE, RIGHT--?

MEMORY TAPE CORROBORATES. PRESENCE OF DETRITUS CONFIRMS.

YEAH, AND MAYBE IF I ROOT AROUND IN ALL THIS JUNK...

...MAYBE I CAN FIND SOMETHING *USEFUL*...

YEAH--I SEE SOME PRETTY NEAT STUFF *ALREADY*--!

DIRECTIVE: STATEMENT OF YOUR INTENTIONS IS COMPULSORY TO SUSTAINED SYMBIOTIC HARMONY.

CLAM UP, 'PUTER-- BEFORE I BOOT YER *DIODES* UPSIDE THE BACK OF YER *BIG-WORDS* CIRCUITS. YOU'RE *BUGGIN'* ME LIKE NO SPIDER ON GOOSEFLESH *EVER* DID...

BESIDES, I NEVER IN-VITED YOU INTO MY SKULL IN THE *FIRST* PLACE. SO WHAT'S WITH THE *SYMBIOTIC* JUNK?

HMM...LOOKS LIKE SOME NICE *COIL* THERE...

YEAH...AND THIS OLD *CAR-BUMPER* OUGHTA MAKE A PERFECT *CROSSPIECE*...

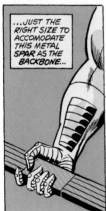

...JUST THE RIGHT SIZE TO ACCOMODATE THIS METAL *SPAR* AS THE *BACKBONE*...

NOW ALL I HAVE TO DO...

...IS SPLICE THE WHOLE SHEBANG *TOGETHER*.

OKAY, 'PUTER, YOU CAN *LEAVE* ANY TIME YOU *WANT*...

...'CUZ ME AN' THE *CROSSBOW* HERE GOT IT ALL *CHECKED OUT*--AND THAT *METAL SLUG* RYKER CALLS A *TANK* IS GONNA WISH IT'D NEVER BEEN *FORGED*.

??????????

...FOR IT IS **YOUR BRAIN** WHICH GUIDES THE DEATH-MACHINE...

...YOUR **MIND** WHICH **FEEDS** IT...

...YOUR MIND WHICH **CONTROLS** THE TANK AND FORCES IT **ONWARD**--EVER ONWARD IN **PURSUIT** OF ITS GROTESQUE **PREY**...

IT IS **YOUR** MIND, NINA, WHICH WILL **DESTROY** DEATHLOK!

BUT NOW, MY DEAR, I MUST **LEAVE** YOU FOR A WHILE. IT IS TIME TO UNDERTAKE YET **ANOTHER** STEP TOWARD MY **ULTIMATE** GOAL...THAT OF **TRANSFORMING** MYSELF INTO...

THE **SAVIOR-MACHINE.**

DO YOU WISH TO REVIEW THE OMNI-COMPUTER'S TAPED OBSERVATIONS OF **MIKE TRAVERS,** MAJOR RYKER?

NOT **NOW,** YOU FOOL--! TRAVERS WILL **KEEP!** I'LL REVIEW THE TAPES **LATER**--AT MY LEISURE.

RIGHT **NOW** WE'LL GET ON WITH THE NEXT PHASE IN **OPERATION: SAVIOR-MACHINE.**

YES, SIR. THE SURGERY ROOM IS **READY.**

TERMINAL EYE: WARNING: SUBJECT MIKE TRAVERS HAS NOW ESCAPED FROM BUILDING. ALERT: SUPER-RED. REPEAT--ALERT: SUPER-RED. RECAPTURE CONTINGENT ON IMMEDIATE AND RADICAL ACTION. ACKNOWLEDGE. REPEAT: ACKNOWLEDGE. ARE YOU LISTENING...?

PANAM

THANK GOD, I **MADE** IT--!

RYKER'S ABSOLUTELY **INSANE**...

GOT TO GET TO **LUTHER**--TRY TO **HELP** HIM...

...AND I'VE **GOT** TO GET HIM **FAST**--BEFORE THE **CANNIBALS** GET TO **ME!**

MAJOR RYKER...*SIR*...ARE YOU *CERTAIN*...YOU WANT TO GO *THROUGH* WITH THIS...? I MEAN, BEING A CYBORG *ALREADY*, DON'T YOU THINK--

NO I *DON'T*--! AND SHOULD YOU PRESUME TO QUESTION MY MOTIVES EVER *AGAIN*--

--JUST REMEMBER THAT YOU *COULD* AWAKEN TO FIND YOUR *OWN* BRAIN LOCKED UP INSIDE SOME COLD GRAY *MACHINE*!

YOU'RE PAID TO *OPERATE*--*NOT TO THINK*! AND YOU WILL OPERATE *RIGHT NOW*--!!

YES, SIR.

HE'S *GOTTA* BE UP *THERE*--IN THE *CRYOGENICS* BUILDING.

YEAH--WAITIN' TO *AMBUSH* US. I DON'T *LIKE* IT! I DON'T LIKE IT AT *ALL*--!

BESIDES, THIS JOINT GIVES ME THE *CREEPS*...

YOU KNOW WHAT THEY USED TO *CALL* THIS PLACE--? *THE FLESH FACTORY*. YEAH, THE FLESH FACTORY...

...BECAUSE THEY USED TO *MANUFACTURE* THINGS HERE--FROM PIECES OF *BODIES*...FROM *LIVING FLESH*...

I DON'T *LIKE* IT...

SHADDUP, YOU YELLOW-SPINED *JERK*. THE ONLY BODY IN HERE *NOW* BELONGS TO THE *DEATHLOK CYBORG*...

...AND HE'S *GOTTA* BE IN *THERE*! SO UNLESS YOU WANT *RYKER* TO MANU- FACTURE SOMETHING OUTTA *YOUR* LIVING FLESH--

--YOU'RE GONNA *STICK WITH US* UNTIL WE FREEZE DEATHLOK FOR *GOOD*--!

OPERATING ROOM

WARNING--

REMAINING THREE ASSASSINS NOW APPROACHING.

YEAH.

EACH SUBJECT ARMED WITH A HIGH-INTENSITY MAXIMUM-DESTRUCTIVE LASER WEAPON.

YEAH.

OUTMODED, OBSOLETE REPEATING BALLISTIC REVOLVERS ARE IN NO WAY ANALOGUED AS EQUIVALENT OR COMPETITIVE WEAPONRY.

YEAH.

PROBABILITY OF FAILURE, INJURY, DISFUNCTION AND/OR TERMINATION OF LIFELINE: 89.75%.

YEAH.

...BUT SO WHAT?

HELLO, SUCKERS...

WHA··?!

AND GOODBYE...

...SUCKERS.

WARNING: THIRD ASSASSIN REMAINS EXTANT!!

DON'T WORRY YOUR LITTLE INPUTS ABOUT IT, 'PUTER. I SAW 'IM SLINK OFF.

NEXT ISSUE: THE FLESH FAILURES!!

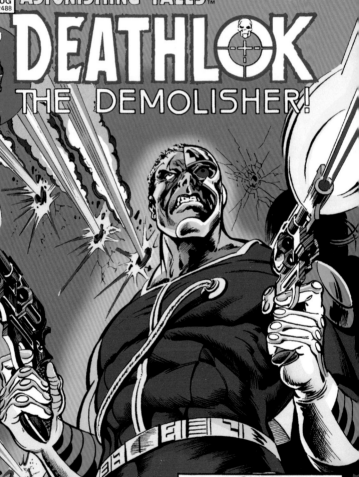

Once you were *Luther Manning*. Once you shared your life with a wife and child, now you share your "life" with a machine. Once you were a man of flesh and blood, now you are only a *cyborg*, a half-human mechanism programmed solely for destruction...yet unable to destroy YOURSELF!

Stan Lee PRESENTS: DEATHLOK THE DEMOLISHER! ™

WRITER
DOUG MOENCH
ARTISTS
RICH BUCKLER AND KEITH POLLARD

OVERVIEW: PAST EVENTS DICTATE--

--THAT I GET SICK 'PUTER.

OUT-STINKIN' SICK.

KLAUS JANSON
INKER
JANICE CHIANG
LETTERER
JANICE COHEN
COLORIST
LEN WEIN
EDITOR

TWICE REMOVED FROM YESTERDAY...

WANNA HEAR ME GO *BANANAS*, 'PUTER?

LISTEN.

THE *DEATH-MACHINE* IS *DEAD!* LONG *LIVE* THE *DEATH MACHINE!!*

ANOMALY: STATUS OF DEATH IMPLIES FORMER STATUS OF LIFE. THE MECHANISM APPELLATED "DEATH MACHINE" WAS AND IS A NON-LIVING UNIT.

YEAH, JUST A *TANK*... WITH NOBODY *INSIDE*...

JUST A HULK OF *COLD METAL* WITH NOTHING INSIDE TO *GUIDE* IT... NOTHING BUT THE URGE TO *KILL*...

LIKE *ME,* PUTER...

...JUST LIKE *ME*...

OMNI-COMPUTER TERMINAL EYE READOUT ON ESCAPED SUBJECT MIKE TRAVERS: CONTINUING HIS SEARCH FOR THE CYBORG DEATHLOK, SUBJECT HAS LOCATED THE SLAIN REBEL LINC SHANE AND NOW PROCEEDS ARMED ON A GO COURSE INDICATING SUCCESS.

HOLE IN A WALL *THAT* SIZE...AND LUTHER *MUST* HAVE BEEN INVOLVED...

DON'T KNOW WHO THIS POOR GUY *WAS*...BUT IN HIS *CONDITION*...

...AND HE'LL BE NEEDING HIS WEAPON A LOT *LESS* THAN *I* WILL.

TRACKS ARE *DEEP TOO* DEEP FOR A *NORMAL* MAN...

...BUT JUST *RIGHT* FOR LUTHER'S *QUARTER-TON CYBORG FRAME.*

WARNING: POSSIBLE PURSUANT APPROACHING RAPIDLY.

I CAN *HEAR HEELS*, 'PUTER.

...AND I *DON'T NEED* YOU TO SAY *WHEN*.

NOW.

YOU JUST WON'T *QUIT*, WILLYA?

ALL RIGHT, TURKEY--

--HAPPY *THANKSGIVING*

WAIT-- LUTHER-- IS THAT *YOU--?*

THOUGHT YOU WERE *DEAD*, MIKE. GLAD TO SEE I WAS *WRONG...AND SORRY* IF I DON'T *SOUND* IT...

IT'S ME -- IT'S *MIKE TRAVERS*

GUESS I'VE TURNED *CRYBABY*, MIKE...

FEELIN' *SORRY* FOR MYSELF... CAN'T THINK ABOUT ANYTHING EXCEPT FINDIN' THAT *SURGEON* ...GETTIN' MYSELF *NORMAL* AGAIN...SO I CAN FACE MY *WIFE* AND *KID* AGAIN...WITHOUT MAKIN' 'EM *SICK*...

LUTHER... WE'LL HAVE TO CHANGE MORE THAN YOUR *FACE* BEFORE YOU CAN GO BACK...

I COULDN'T TELL YOU *BEFORE* LUTHER, BUT...WELL *JANICE* AND I....WE...

...SIX *MONTHS* AGO...

SHUT *UP*, MIKE--DON'T *SAY* IT...

NO...

LUTHER--FOR *GOD'S SAKE*, MAN, IT'S BEEN *FIVE YEARS--! FIVE YEARS*, LUTHER...

YOU WERE *DEAD*. WHAT WERE WE SUPPOSED TO--

NOOO!!!...

YOU TOOK *THEM, TOO?*

AFTER THEY TOOK MY *BODY* --HALF MY *BRAIN*--ALL MY *FEELING*--??!

NO LUTHER-- YOU *CAN* FEEL!

YOU'RE *PROVING* IT RIGHT *NOW*--

SHUT UP, TRAVERS! YOU WERE SUPPOSED TO BE MY *BEST FRIEND*--BUT INSTEAD YOU *RIPPED OFF* THE LAST SHRED OF THE PAST I *HAD!* YOU EVEN KILLED MY *HOPE*--!

I GOT *NOTHIN'* NOW-- EXCEPT AN ITCH TO BUST YOUR *SKULL* INTO *EGGSHELL!*

OBSERVATION: THE EXTIRPATION OF SUBJECT MICHAEL TRAVERS SERVES NO LOGICAL PURPOSE THEREFORE CONSTITUTING AN UNNECESSARY EXPENDITURE OF BIONIC ENERGY.

ALL RIGHT, LUTHER--I'LL *GROVEL* IF THAT'S WHAT YOU *WANT* YOU STUPID *JACKASS* BECAUSE *I* WANT TO *LIVE*...

...JUST LIKE *YOU* WANTED TO LIVE WHEN I *SAVED* *YOUR LIFE* FROM THAT 'CUSSION BOMB

I'LL SAY IT *AGAIN*, LUTHER-- IT WAS *FIVE YEARS*...

YOU WERE OFFICIALLY DECLARED *DEAD* YOU *ARE* DEAD!

SUBJECT TRAVERS' ASSERTION TECHNICALLY AND CONCEPTUALLY CORRECT.

YEAH, MAYBE I *AM* DEAD...MAYBE IT'S JUST THIS STINKIN' *BODY* THAT KEEPS GETTIN' IN THE *WAY CONFUSIN'* THINGS...

ALL *RIGHT*, MIKE.

RIGHT NOW YOU'RE LOWER THAN *SCUM* TO ME...

BUT YOU *DID* SAVE MY LIFE.

SO I'LL LET YOU *KEEP YOURS*...

...UNTIL THE NEXT TIME I SEE YOUR MOTHER-LOVIN' *TAIL* HERE IN *MANHATTAN* OR *ANYWHERE ELSE.*

REMEMBER THAT...*SCUM.*

TERMINAL EYE READOUT: RELOCKING POSITION OF CYBORG DEATHLOK... LOWER MANHATTAN. PRECISE COORDINATES RECORDED ON ANCILLARY DATA SHEETS.

HOW COULD SHE *DO* IT TO ME, 'PUTER?

HOW COULD SHE--

HUH? WHAT'S *THAT*?

SOUNDS LIKE A--

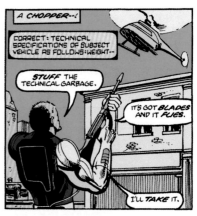

A *CHOPPER*--!

CORRECT: TECHNICAL SPECIFICATIONS OF SUBJECT VEHICLE AS FOLLOWS: WEIGHT--

STUFF THE TECHNICAL GARBAGE.

IT'S GOT *BLADES* AND IT *FLIES*.

I'LL *TAKE* IT.

--BUT ARE YOU *SURE* THIS IS THE SURGEON WHO WORKED ON THAT *DEATHLOK* GOON!

WHAT THE--?

COURSE I'M SURE. WOULD I TAKE ALL THIS NICE CRISP *BREAD* FROM YOU IF I DIDN'T HAVE THE AUTHENTIC *GOODS*...?

THAT'S WHAT *QUARTUCCIO* WANTS TO KNOW.

SO WHY DON'T YOU *PROVE* IT BY DELIVERIN' THE GOODS TO HIS *PENTHOUSE*...

WELL? WHAT ARE YOU AND YOUR THUGS *WAITIN'* FOR? YOU *GOT* YOUR MONEY...

SO AIN'T IT ABOUT TIME YOU WENT AND GOT THE *CYBORG-DOC?*

YEAH, GUESS QUARTUCCIO *DESERVES* HIS DAY-OFF...

BUT FIRST, WE GOT A LITTLE SOMETHIN' FOR *YOU*, SUMMERS..

'PUTER, THIS LOOKS LIKE IT'S JUST ABOUT TO GET *INTERESTING*...

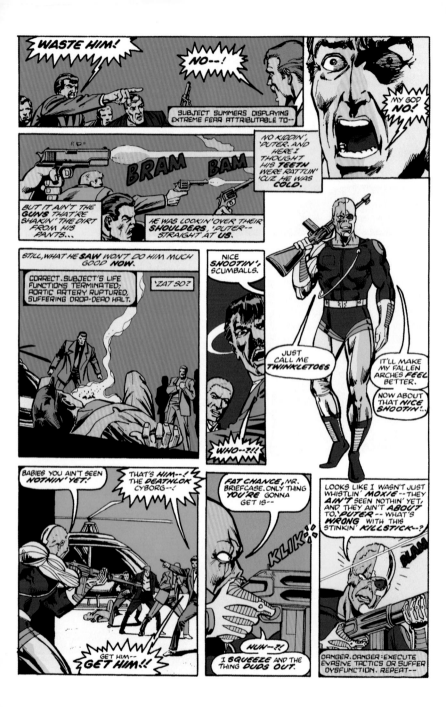

ALL *RIGHT* ALREADY! I'M *DIVIN'*--I'M *DIVIN'*--!!

AND ON THE *WAY* YOU CAN START ANSWERING MY *QUESTION!*

REQUEST INIMICAL TO SURVIVAL TACTICS. FUNDAMENTAL PROGRAMMING CLEARLY PROHIBITS EXTRANEOUS DATA OUTPUT IN SITUATIONS OF PERSISTING DANGER.

PRESENCE OF EXTANT THREAT DICTATES--

BLAM BRAM BLAM

THAT YOU ANSWER THE *QUESTION* BEFORE I RIP *YOUR* GUTS RIGHT OUTTA *MINE!*

SUBJECT WEAPON'S POWER CRYSTAL NOW VOID-- ENERGY DEPLETED. CONCLUSION: WEAPON USELESS.

SPEENG CHEW

OF ALL THE *STINKIN' SLIMY, LOUSY, DIRTY ROTTEN*--

HALT. REPEAT: HALT. EMOTION--

WHADDAYA MEAN *HALT?* I'VE BEEN LUGGIN' THIS BLOODY *LASER-RIFLE* ALL OVER MANHATTAN AND IT DOESN'T EVEN *WORK*--! WOULDN'T *YOU* BE MAD, 'PUTER?

IRREVELANT. PRESENT CIRCUMSTANCES REQUIRE ATTENTION-FOCUS MAXIMUM.

Y'MEAN THIS RING-AROUND-THE-ROSIE *MERRY-GO-ROUND*--?

CONTINGENCY DEATH-THREAT ORIGINATES FROM THREE SEPARATE COORDINATES. EMERGENCY PROXIMITY OF FIRST ADVERSARY.

IS *THAT* ALL THAT'S BUGGIN' YA? I CAN *HEAR* WHICH ONE'S COMIN' *CLOSEST* 'PUTER...

...SCUFFLIN' TOWARD THE *CORNER* LIKE AN INCHWORM AFRAID OF FINDIN' A *RATTLER.*

...I THINK I'LL TAKE THE *EASY* WAY OUT...

BUT SINCE I GOTTA *PUNCH HIS FACE* BEFORE HIS *GUN* TURNS THE CORNER AND BLASTS *MINE...*

...AND LET THE *CORNER* PUNCH HIS FACE!

SROTCH!

SUCCESS REPORT: EXCELLENT.

TRAJECTORY OF WALL FRAGMENT ESTIMATED WITH NEAR PRECISION.

THANKS FOR THE *BACK-PAT*, 'PUTER. NICE TO *HEAR* COMIN' FROM *YOU*. 'COURSE, *STILL* I HATE YOUR FRUITY *NUTS-AND-BOLTS* GUTS.

WAIT A MINUTE, *TOOTS*-- I GOT BAD *NEWS* FOR YA...

PLAYIN' WITH *GUNS*--

--CAN GET YA *HURT*.

GUHHH!

WARNING: SECONDARY ADVERSARY APPROACHING.

--FROM *BEHIND*.

YEAH, I *KNOW*.

AND THAT'S EXACTLY WHERE HE'S GONNA *LAND*...

ON HIS.

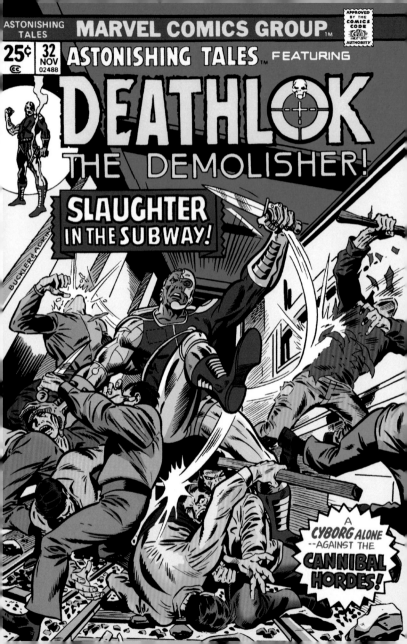

Once you were *Luther Manning*. Once you shared your life with a wife and child, now you share your "life" with a machine. Once you were a man of flesh and blood, now you are only a *cyborg*, a half-human mechanism programmed solely for destruction...yet unable to destroy YOURSELF!

Stan Lee PRESENTS: DEATHLOK THE DEMOLISHER!
™

The MAN WHO SOLD the WORLD!

HELICOPTER AT HEIGHT OF THIRTY-FIVE FEET AND CLIMBING. A JUMP AT THIS JUNCTURE WOULD BE PROHIBITIVE--

YOU MEAN I WON'T MAKE IT, EVEN IF I TRY? RIGHT, 'PUTER?

AFFIRMATIVE.

YOU'RE A FATALIST. WHAT HAPPENS IF I DON'T TRY SOMETHING, AT LEAST?

45 CALIBER AUTOMATIC OUT OF AMMUNITION. ONLY WEAPON AVAILABLE--

WAY AHEAD OF YOU. I DON'T WEAR THIS "BUTCHER" KNIFE ON MY LEG FOR SHOW, YOU KNOW!

RICH BUCKLER
PLOT, CONCEPT,
SCRIPT: PGS. 1-7

BILL MANTLO
SCRIPT: PGS. 10-30

RICH, KEITH,
BOB McLEOD,
& THE WHOLE
BLAME BULLPEN
ARTWORK

CHARLOTTE J.
LETTERING

JANICE COHEN
COLORING

ANALYSIS: COMPOSITION OF STEEL RAILING NOT SUFFICENT TO--

I..DON'T... ...WANT TO... ...HEAR IT.

OMNI-COMPUTER READ-OUT: DEATHLOK CYBORG APPROACHING FALLEN HELICOPTER AT COORDINATES X-575MNY. NORTHWEST SECTOR 6

Y'KNOW, 'PUTER, WHAT REALLY *BURNS MY CIRCUITS* IS THAT RYKER IS SOMEHOW *MONITORING* EVERYTHING I'M DOING.

IT AIN'T ENOUGH THAT HE TURNED ME INTO THIS THING OF DEAD FLESH WITH A *COMPUTER ALTER EGO.*

HE COULD BE WATCHING ME RIGHT THIS SECOND, EVEN MANIPULATING THIS WHOLE INCIDENT AND--

WHAT IN HOLY--?

LOOKS LIKE THE *CANNIBALS* IN THIS NEIGHBORHOOD GOT HERE FIRST.

AFFIRMATIVE: TWO CANNIBALS SHOW NO SIGNS OF LIFE FUNCTION. EVIDENCE OF SKIRMISH--

SLAUGHTER IS MORE THE WORD FOR IT! OUR *TARGET* IS ARMED AND DANGEROUS, AS THOSE TWO SLIMY GINZOS FOUND OUT--THE *HARD WAY!*

HOPE RYKER'S GETTING THIS ALL DOWN ON *HOLOGRAMS* FOR POSTERITY. EVERY *LAST* DROP OF *BLOOD* HIS CRUMMY *TERMINAL EYES* CAN FOCUS ON.

--I COULDN'T TELL YOU THIS *BEFORE*, BUT--WELL --*JANICE* AND I--WE--

STOP IT, MIKE! STOP *TALKIN'*!

I SAID, SHUT UP!

--SIX *MONTHS* AGO--

IT'S BEEN *FIVE YEARS* SINCE YOU *DIED*, LUTHER!

FOR *GOD'S* SAKE, LUTHER--

STINKIN', FILTHY, BACKSTABBIN' DIRTY *SON OF A*--

--*THEM, TOO?* YOU TOOK *THEM* AWAY FROM ME, TOO!

YOU'RE *PROVING THAT* RIGHT NOW--

--MMPPFFF!

YOU SAVED MY *LIFE*, TRAVERS-- ONCE--A LONG TIME AGO! YOU CAN *KEEP YOURS* NOW--

--BUT IF I EVER RUN ACROSS YOU *AGAIN*, SCUM--

A CYBORG CAN'T *FEEL*, TRAVERS! IT *CAN'T!* NOT THE WAY YOU GOT *ME FEELIN'!*

SHUT UP SNAKE!

YOU'RE *WRONG*, LUTHER! YOU *CAN* FEEL!

TIME 0725. CYBORG-DESIGNATE DEATHLOK LEAVES SUBJECT- DESIGNATE TRAVERS. PROCEEDS TO...

THAT'S ALL, SOLDIER! I HAVEN'T GOT *TIME* FOR THE *REST!*

THE OMNI- COMPUTER CAN KEEP AN *'EYE'* ON DEATHLOK AND TRAVERS--AS WELL AS DEAL WITH ANY *EMERGENCIES!*

I DON'T THINK THAT *EITHER* OF THEM RERESENTS ANY SORT OF *THREAT* AT THE PRESENT TIME!

GET THE COMPUTER TO ASSEMBLE A *READ OUT* ON A MAN NAMED *VICTORIO QUARTUCCIO!* HE MAY HAVE USED *OTHER* NAMES-- SO I'LL WANT A *FULL DOSSIER!*

AS FOR LUTHER MANNING--I'LL DEAL WITH HIM *LATER!*

AFTER THE *OPERATION!*

IF EVERYTHING GOES *RIGHT*, IT JUST MAY BE THAT *DEATH- LOK* WILL NEVER BE A *PROBLEM* AGAIN!

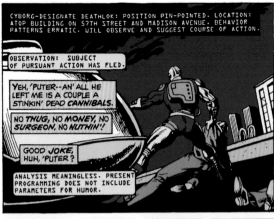

CYBORG-DESIGNATE DEATHLOK: POSITION PIN-POINTED. LOCATION: ATOP BUILDING ON 57TH STREET AND MADISON AVENUE. BEHAVIOR PATTERNS ERRATIC. WILL OBSERVE AND SUGGEST COURSE OF ACTION.

OBSERVATION: SUBJECT OF PURSUANT ACTION HAS FLED.

YEH, 'PUTER--AN' ALL HE LEFT ME IS A COUPLE A STINKIN' DEAD *CANNIBALS*.

NO *THUG*, NO *MONEY*, NO *SURGEON*, NO *NUTHIN'*!

GOOD *JOKE*, HUH, 'PUTER?

ANALYSIS MEANINGLESS. PRESENT PROGRAMMING DOES NOT INCLUDE PARAMETERS FOR HUMOR.

THEN THE PRESENT PARAMETERS *STINK*, 'PUTER. THEY STINK TO *HIGH-HEAVEN*!

YOU HEAR ME, *WIND*? *CITY*? *NIGHT*?

RYKER?

THEY *STINK*!

BEHAVIOR IRRATIONAL.

SO WHAT?

TARGET-SUBJECT MAY ESCAPE.

GOOD *ANSWER*! ALRIGHT, 'PUTER --HOW DO YOU DETECT FOOT-PRINTS ON *CONCRETE*?

WE USE OUR EYES.

VERY *FUNNY*, 'PUTER! SO YOU *DO* KNOW WHAT A *JOKE IS*!

INFRARED SEEKING PATTERN ACTIVATED IN BIONIC EYE.

HEY! YOU *WEREN'T* JOKING!

FOOT-PRINTS!

CORRECT: IN-FRARED TRACER ESTABLISHES THAT TARGET-SUBJECT HAS NOT BEEN GONE MORE THAN FIVE MINUTES.

ESTIMATED CHANCES OF INTERCEPT AND APPREHENSION: 97%.

WAY TO *GO*, 'PUTER! SO ALL I GOTTA DO IS FOLLOW HIS TRACKS AS HE *HOT-FOOTS* IT ACROSS TOWN!

CORRECT:

NOT BAD! IF I DIDN'T HATE YOUR MECHANI-CAL *GUTS*, 'PUTER, I MIGHT GET TO *LIKE YOU!*

IRRELEVANT.

YEAH, IT *WAS*, WASN'T IT?

OH WELL... YOU CAN'T WIN 'EM *ALL*!

JUST DON'T EVER PULL A *SWITCH* ONE DAY AN' START *LAUGHIN'* ALONG WITH ME...*OK*, 'PUTER?

I MEAN...IF I EVER GOT THE FEELIN' THAT YOU'RE BECOMIN' AS *HUMAN* AS ME, I DON'T THINK I COULD *TAKE IT!*

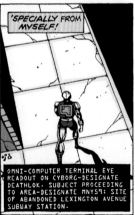

'SPECIALLY FROM *MYSELF!*

OMNI-COMPUTER TERMINAL EYE READOUT ON CYBORG-DESIGNATE DEATHLOK. SUBJECT PROCEEDING TO AREA-DESIGNATE MNY59: SITE OF ABANDONED LEXINGTON AVENUE SUBWAY STATION.

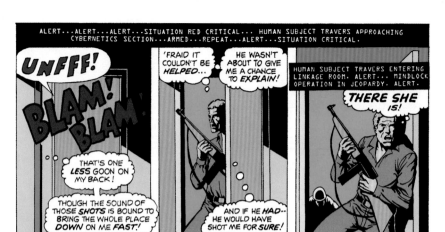

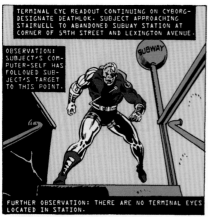

TERMINAL EYE READOUT CONTINUING ON CYBORG-DESIGNATE DEATHLOK. SUBJECT APPROACHING STAIRWELL TO ABANDONED SUBWAY STATION AT CORNER OF 59TH STREET AND LEXINGTON AVENUE.

OBSERVATION: SUBJECT'S COMPUTER-SELF HAS FOLLOWED SUBJECT'S TARGET TO THIS POINT.

SUBWAY

FURTHER OBSERVATION: THERE ARE NO TERMINAL EYES LOCATED IN STATION.

CONCLUSION: FURTHER TRACKING OF CYBORG-DESIGNATE DEATHLOK IMPOSSIBLE.

ALERT: POSSIBILITY OF TARGET WITHIN SUBWAY: 78.00097%

AN' HE'S *ARMED,* 'PUTER--AN' *HURT!* THERE WAS *BLOOD* ALONGSIDE THEM FOOTPRINTS THE LAST COUPLE'A *BLOCKS.*

CORRECT. TARGET-SUBJECT'S CAPACITY FOR DAMAGE TO THIS MECHANISM ESTIMATED AT...

STOW IT, 'PUTER! I *KNOW* HOW DANGEROUS A TRAPPED AN' *WOUNDED* ANIMAL CAN BE!

HE'LL FIGHT TO GET RID O' *ME* AS HARD AS *I'M* FIGHTIN' TO GET RID O' *YOU,* 'PUTER!

ILLOGICAL. THERE IS NO #1' IN THIS ENTITY. 'WE' ARE ONE.

THAT DON'T STOP ME FROM *WISHIN'!* 'PUTER!

HOLD IT! LOOKS LIKE WE *FOUND* OUR BOY!

OBSERVATION: WE ARE NOT THE FIRST.

SO I *SEE,* 'PUTER! COUPLE'A *SEWER RATS* ABOUT TO KILL OFF MY ONE SHOT AT FINDIN' THE *FACE-DOCTOR!*

NO WAY, 'PUTER!

KILL HIM! WE HAVE BEEN *COMMANDED!*

NO WAY!

OBSERVATION: TAR-GET SUBJECT HAS BEEN STABBED REPEATEDLY IN CHEST. RATE OF LOSS OF BLOOD ESTIMATED AT...

LATER, 'PUTER! RIGHT *NOW*--

--I GOT *BUSINESS* TO ATTEND TO!

ANALYSIS OF PRESENT ANTAGONIST: LOBOTOMIZED HUMAN DRONE CONTROLLED FROM OUTSIDE PROGRAMMING.

THEY AIN'T *CANNIBALS*, 'PUTER?

CORRECT.

WHO'S PULLIN' YOUR *STRINGS*, SCUM?

THAT'S A *RELIEF!* I WAS BEGINNIN' TO THINK ALL OF *MANHATTAN* WAS OCCUPIED BY THEM STINKIN' *FLESH EATERS.*

WHO SET YOU ON THE *COURIER?*

WAS IT *RYKER?* ANSWER *ME!*

OBSERVATION: IMPOSSIBLE. SUBJECT'S JAW IS BROKEN.

SENSORS INDICATE THAT TARGET SUBJECT IS DEAD.

NO!

NO!!

YOU CAN'T BE *DEAD! NOT YET!*

YOU AIN'T TOLD ME WHERE TO FIND THE *CYBORG-DOC!* THE GUY WHO CAN MAKE ME LOOK *HUMAN!*

YOU AIN'T DEAD!

HEARTBEAT: NONE. RESPIRATORY ACTION: NONE. ELECTRO-VASCULAR ACTIVITY: NONE...

SHUT UP, 'PUTER!

ALERT: DRONES APPROACH AGAIN. NUMBERS INCREASED.

I SEE 'EM, 'PUTER!

SENSORS INDICATE THAT THIS MECHANISM HAS AN 87.00967% PROBABILITY OF BEING DESTROYED. BEGIN EVASIVE ACTION.

DROP DEAD, 'PUTER! THOSE BIRDS ARE GONNA *PAY!*

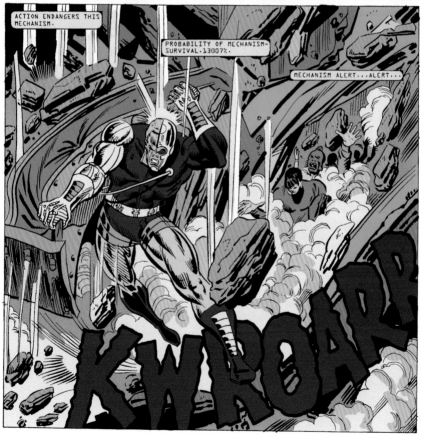

OMNI-COMPUTER TERMINAL EYE READOUT ON ESCAPED SUBJECTS MIKE TRAVERS AND NINA FERRY: MINDLOCK ON FEMALE HUMAN BROKEN... FEMALE **STILL** LINKED THOUGH SUBJECT TRAVERS IS AS YET UNAWARE OF IT.

WE'RE **OUT**, NINA!

RYKER'S **LOST** THIS BATTLE! NEITHER HIS **GOONS**, HIS BLESSED **COMPUTER** OR HIS **BOOBY-TRAPS** COULD HOLD US!

YOU'RE NOT **LISTENING**, NINA!

POOR KID. SHE'S STILL **OUT**--PROBABLY UNDER HEAVY **SEDATION!** THAT'S **ANOTHER ONE** I OWE YOU, RYKER!

O.K., NINA, YOU REST UP--

--WHILE I DO THE WORK FOR THE **BOTH** OF US!

AND MAYBE--JUST **MAYBE**--WHEN YOU WAKE UP YOU'LL BE ABLE TO TELL ME WHERE TO FIND THE **DOC** THAT WORKED ON **LUTHER!**

SUBJECT TRAVERS STILL UNAWARE THAT HE IS BEING MONITORED BY LINKAGE IN SUBJECT FERRY'S BRAIN.

THERE GO SOME MORE OF RYKER'S **GOONS!**

BUT WE'LL BE **LONG GONE** BEFORE THEY CATCH ONTO OUR **TRAIL**, NINA!

CONSTANT TRACKING PATTERN ESTABLISHED.

FEMALE IS NOW A TERMINAL OUTLET FOR OMNI-COMPUTER COMPLEX. LINKAGE FUNCTIONING AND COMPLETE.

JUST TRUST ME, NINA!

RYKER AIN'T GONNA GET AT YOU **AGAIN!** NOT IF **I** CAN **HELP IT!**

[126]

WE'RE OUT, 'PUTER! WITHOUT A *SCRATCH!*

ELEMENT OF RISK TOO HIGH. FURTHER ACTION TO BE AVOIDED IN FUTURE.

BWAY
OWN—QUEENS
LAND-BRONX

DID *I* ASK THOSE DRONES TO *JUMP* ON ME, 'PUTER?

THEN KEEP YOUR *ADVICE* TO YOURSELF--BESIDES--

--I GOT PART OF WHAT I *CAME* FOR!

THE MONEY! THIS BAG FULL O' *GREEN* IS GONNA BUY ME A *NEW KISSER,* 'PUTER!

NEGATIVE.

WHAT ARE YOU *TALKIN'* ABOUT?

WHY NOT?

BIONIC EYE ANALYSIS SHOWS LINEN UPON WHICH MONEY HAS BEEN PRINTED IS NOT GOVERNMENT STOCK.

YA MEAN IT'S *COUNTERFEIT?*

AFFIRMATIVE.

DAMN!

ALL RIGHT, 'PUTER! SO THE DOUGH'S *FAKE!* SO WHAT?

THE *DOC* WANTED IT FOR *SOMETHING,* SO I'M GONNA *DELIVER* IT TO HIM!

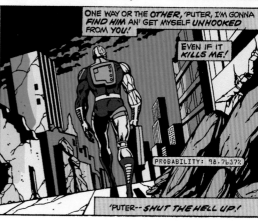

ONE WAY OR THE *OTHER,* 'PUTER, I'M GONNA *FIND HIM* AN' GET MYSELF *UNHOOKED* FROM YOU!

EVEN IF IT *KILLS ME!*

PROBABILITY: 98.7637%

'PUTER-- *SHUT THE HELL UP!*

A man locked in DEATH, No—not a MAN—a mockery of a man, an amalgam of flesh and computer-circuitry that is the cyborg-designate DEATHLOK. Luther Manning has died and now, RESURRECTED in the year 1990, he searches with the fragment of humanity LEFT in him for a way to save both HIMSELF and his very SANITY.

Stan Lee PRESENTS: DEATHLOK THE DEMOLISHER! ™

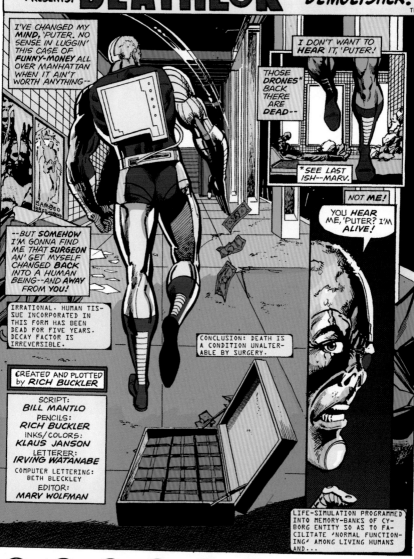

I'VE CHANGED MY MIND, 'PUTER. NO SENSE IN LUGGIN' THIS CASE OF FUNNY-MONEY ALL OVER MANHATTAN WHEN IT AIN'T WORTH ANYTHING—

I DON'T WANT TO HEAR IT, 'PUTER!

THOSE DRONES* BACK THERE ARE DEAD—

* SEE LAST ISH—MARV.

NOT ME!

YOU HEAR ME, 'PUTER? I'M ALIVE!

—BUT SOMEHOW I'M GONNA FIND ME THAT SURGEON AN' GET MYSELF CHANGED BACK INTO A HUMAN BEING—AND AWAY FROM YOU!

IRRATIONAL. HUMAN TISSUE INCORPORATED IN THIS FORM HAS BEEN DEAD FOR FIVE YEARS. DECAY FACTOR IS IRREVERSIBLE.

CONCLUSION: DEATH IS A CONDITION UNALTERABLE BY SURGERY.

CREATED AND PLOTTED by RICH BUCKLER

SCRIPT: BILL MANTLO
PENCILS: RICH BUCKLER
INKS/COLORS: KLAUS JANSON
LETTERER: IRVING WATANABE
COMPUTER LETTERING: BETH BLECKLEY
EDITOR: MARV WOLFMAN

LIFE-SIMULATION PROGRAMMED INTO MEMORY-BANKS OF CYBORG ENTITY SO AS TO FACILITATE 'NORMAL FUNCTIONING' AMONG LIVING HUMANS AND...

DRY UP, HUH, 'PUTER?

AN' WHILE WE WERE *ARGUIN'* --I DECIDED TO TAKE THIS STUFF ALONG--

JUST IN *CASE!*

IN CASE *WHAT?*

IF THOSE DRONES I WIPED OUT COULDN'T *THINK*-- THEN WHAT MADE 'EM ATTACK THE *COURIER?*

AN' IF THIS STUFF WAS *COUNTER-FEIT*--

--WHY DID THE JOKER GET HIMSELF *KILLED* FERRYIN' IT AROUND?

IT DON'T ADD *UP*, 'PUTER!

WARNING. PRESENT COURSE DOES NOT COMPUTE.

CONCENTRATION OF CANNIBALS IN AREA IS HIGH-PROBABILITY. ADDED WEIGHT OF FALSE CURRENCY UNNECESSARY.

'CEPT THAT I'M TAKIN' IT ALONG *ANYWAY*-- NECESSARY OR *NOT*.

AND WHY THE BLAZES DO THOSE STINKIN' *FLESH-EATERS* FOLLOW ME AROUND WHEREVER I GO? WHAT'RE THEY *AFTER*, 'PUTER?

CANNIBALS ARE DRAWN TO ODOR EMITTED BY DECAYING FLESH AND CHEMICAL PRESERVA-TIVE FLUID OF THIS ENTITY.

YOU MEAN THEY SMELL A *CORPSE*, DON'T YOU, 'PUTER?

THEY SMELL *ME?*

AFFIRMATIVE.

OH GOD...

...WHY?

[130]

OMNI-COMPUTER TERMINAL EYE READOUT ON CYBORG DESIGNATE 'DEATHLOK'. SUBJECT HAS APPARENTLY REAL-IZED THE USELESSNESS OF COUNTERFEIT CURRENCY RETRIEVED FROM DEAD COURIER...SUBJECT IS IN AN EX-TREMELY AGITATED STATE...OVER-RIDING IMPULSES FROM HIS INTERNAL COMPUTER.

AN' IF HE'S *OUT THERE*--THERE AIN'T *NO* AMOUNT OF MONEY CAN *BUY* HIM!

'CAUSE RYKER'LL HAVE HIM RUNNIN' *SCARED*--

--*TOO* SCARED TA TAKE A CHANCE ON *HELPIN'* ME!

I KNOW YOU'RE *LISTENIN'*, RYKER! I KNOW THAT IT WAS *YOU* BEHIND EVERY STINKIN' THING THAT'S EVER *HAPPENED* TO ME!

AN' I'M COMIN' TO *GET* YOU, MAJOR!

THIS 'COPTER I *ACED** CAN BE *FIXED* WITH-OUT TOO MUCH SWEAT ...AND ONCE I FIX IT I'LL *FIND* YOU, RYKER!

I *SWEAR* IT!

**LAST ISH--MARV.*

OMNI-COMPUTER SURGERY TERM-INAL EYE READOUT ON PATIENT-SUBJECT DESIGNATE 'SIMON RYKER'. PATIENT IS AT PRESENT IN STATE OF HOMEOSTASIS...ALL ORGANIC ACTIVITY ON INPUT-RECEPTOR STATUS...SYNAPSE-LINKAGES FIRING DATA AT ACCELERATED CUMULA-TIVE INPUT LEVEL FOR FUTURE TERMINAL BANK STORAGE...BODILY FUNCTIONS RAISED TO COMPENSATE FOR POSSIBLE ORGANIC OVERLOAD ...FOLLOWING...

THE COMPUTER IS MAKING DAMN SURE THAT HE DOESN'T *BURN OUT*, DOCTOR!

A SLIGHT *ADJUSTMENT* IN ITS PROGRAMMING COULD INSURE THAT IT *MISCALCULATES* SLIGHTLY AND--

I THINK YOU'D BETTER *SHUT UP*, DOCTOR!

MAJOR RYKER HAS BEEN ON TOTAL *MIND-LOCK* FOR SEVERAL *HOURS* NOW...

...WHICH MEANS THAT ANY-THING AND *EVERYTHING* THAT EITHER YOU OR I MAY SAY IS BEING *RECORDED* AND *RETAINED*--!

OH MY *LORD!* YOU MEAN--

I MEAN THAT WHEN HE *AWAKES*--AND HE *WILL* WAKE, DOCTOR--I *ASSURE* YOU OF THAT--

--I WOULD *SUGGEST* THAT YOU BE AS FAR *AWAY* FROM HERE AS *POSSIBLE!*

BECAUSE, DOCTOR, THE OMNI-COMPUTER HAS FAITHFULLY *IMPRINTED* YOUR FEW ILL-CHOSEN WORDS OF *TREACHERY* ON THE CIRCUITRY THAT NOW EMCOMPASSES PART OF MAJOR RYKER'S *MEMORY PATTERNS*--

--AND I *PITY* YOU WHEN MAJOR RYKER *COMES TO!*

THE THREE *PRE-PARATORY* OPER-ATIONS WERE CHILD'S-PLAY COMPARED TO THIS *NEXT* ONE, GENTLEMEN--

--AND ONE *SLIP-UP* NOW COULD EASILY *KILL* MAJOR RYKER--

--OR *US*--IF THE COMPUTER, OF WHICH RYKER NOW IS A *PART* SO *DECIDES!*

ALL LINKAGES ESTABLISHED AND FUNCTIONING. SUBJECT DESIGNATE 'RYKER' PRIMED AND READY FOR STAGE FOUR.

SUBJECT DESIGNATE 'RYKER' IN NEURO-SEDATION. CARDIO-VASCULAR ACTIVITY STILLED.

NOW, GENTLEMEN... HIS HEART IS *STOPPED!* MAJOR RYKER IS TOTALLY *ANESTHETIZED!*

ER--DR.LEMNER HAS *LEFT,* SIR. SHALL I--?

NO, DR. BLAINE. HE WASN'T *NEEDED.*

SHALL WE *BEGIN,* DOCTOR?

OMNI-COMPUTER EYE READOUT.

CYBORG DESIGNATE 'DEATHLOK' HAS MANAGED TO RE-PAIR HELICOPTER AND IS HEADING AWAY FROM MANHAT-TAN SECTOR. CAL-CULATED IN-FLIGHT TRAJECTORY ESTAB-LISHES PROBABLE DESTINATION COOR-DINATES AS BEING IN THE AREA OF SECTOR LI11569.

LONG ISLAND, 'PUTER?

AFFIRMATIVE. HEL-ICOPTER AUTO-CON-TROLS LOCKED ON AN AREA NEAR LONG IS-LAND SOUND. DES-TINATION PROGRAMME PRERECORDED AND IR-REVERSIBLE.

THEN THAT'S WHERE THE *COURIER* WAS *HEADED!* HE PROBABLY LOCKED THE *CONTROLS* SO GROUND INTERFER-ENCE WOULDN'T BE *POSSIBLE!* SMART COOKIE--BUT NOT TOO SMART OR HE WOULDN'T BE *DEAD!*

AN' ALL THAT TIME I SPENT *TRAILIN'* HIM I COULDA JUST HOPPED INTO THIS *COPTER* AN' GONE STRAIGHT TO WHERE HE WAS GOING *WITHOUT HIM!*

AFFIRMATIVE.

TELL ME SOMETHIN', 'PUTER--

--DID YOU KNOW THAT ALL *ALONG?*

AFFIRMATIVE.

ANY REASON YOU DIDN'T *TELL* ME?

NOT PROGRAMMED TO RESPOND TO SPECIFIC QUESTIONS UNLESS SUCH QUERIES ARE VOICE AND/OR INTERNALLY VOCALIZED.

IN *OTHER* WORDS-- BECAUSE I DIDN'T *ASK??!*

THAT'S GREAT, 'PUTER. JUST *GREAT!*

PRE-CODED LANDING COORDINATES ACTIVATED AUTOMATICALLY. HELICOPTER DESCENDING ACCORDING TO PROGRAMMING.

WE'RE *LANDED,* 'PUTER!

WHERE? THIS PLACE LOOKS LIKE IT COULD PASS FOR THE LONG ISLAND *HILTON!*

MEMORY STORAGE DATA INDICATES ESTATE AS THAT BELONGING TO MAJOR SIMON RYKER.

RYKER??

BUT WHY WOULD THE COURIER BE COMIN' TO *HIM?*

INSUFFICIENT DATA TO...

DON'T **WORRY** ABOUT IT, 'PUTER!

IF RYKER'S **IN THERE**--

--I WON'T **NEED** ANY DATA FOR WHAT I'M GONNA **DO** TO HIM!

OBSERVATION: WEIGHT OF CYBORG FRAME IS DESTROYING THE GRASS BENEATH IT.

GRASS IS REAL... NOT SYNTHETIC.

AT PRESENT INFLA-TIONARY COSTS... ESTIMATED DAMAGE RUNS IN EXCESS OF $300,000.

HELLO, CYBORG. SOMETHIN' WE CAN **DO** FOR YOU?

I WANT **RYKER**, SLUG! WHERE IS HE?

UGLY WANTS TO SEE THE **MAJOR**, BRYCE!

RYKER AIN'T **IN** TO THOSE WHAT AIN'T **EXPECTED**, JERK!

AN' HE AIN'T GONNA **LIKE** WHAT YOU DONE TO HIS **LAWN**, MISTER!

'LESS MAYBE YOU GET DOWN ON YOUR **KNEES** AN' FIX IT **UP!**

OBSERVATION: THUGS IN EM-PLOY OF MAJOR RYKER. MIN-IMAL INTELLIGENCE.

YEAH. SO I **GATHERED**, 'PUTER!

YOU GUNSELS WANT THE LAWN **FIXED**--

--**YOU** FIX IT! NOW GET OUT OF MY **WAY!**

I'M COMIN' **THOUGH!**

WARNING: LIFE SYSTEMS FUNCTIONING AT ONLY 67% CAPACITY.

YOU MEAN I'M WEARING *DOWN*, 'PUTER!

I *TOLD* YOU TO GET OUT OF MY *WAY*, BOY-O'S--

AFFIRMATIVE.

--AN' I *MEANT* IT!

RYKER MUST HAVE THE *DOC* INSIDE! GOT TO *GET* TO HIM!

COMPUTER ANALYSIS REVEALS PRESENCE OF TWO HUMANS WITHIN. CAUTION ADVISED...

TO *HELL* WITH CAUTION, 'PUTER!

ONE OF THEM'S *GOT* TO BE THE *DOC!* THAT'S WHY THE COURIER WAS *HEADED* HERE!

AN' RYKER'S GOONS LEFT THE DOOR *OPEN!*

SENSORS INDICATE 97% POSSIBILITY OF TRAP.

I DON'T *CARE* ANYMORE ABOUT RYKER'S *TRAPS*, 'PUTER. I JUST WANT THE *DOC!*

NOT THIS WAY...THAT LEADS *UPSTAIRS!* SOMETHIN' TELLS ME THAT HE'S IN...

THE *STUDY!* THERE HE *IS*, 'PUTER!

CLICK

I'VE *FOUND* HIM!

STOP!

NO WAY!

HE'S *MINE* NOW, AND--

LOOK AT HIM, DEATHLOK! *LOOK!*

OH GOD! IT--IT'S *ME!* LUTHER MANNING!

CORRECT. NOW, YOU MAY *SHOOT HIM*, IF THAT IS YOUR *WISH*--

--BUT I DON'T THINK EVEN *YOU* WOULD BE UP TO *BLOWING YOUR OWN BRAINS OUT!*

I AM *HELLINGER!*

MEMORY BANKS INDICATE NO KNOWLEDGE OF BEING-DESIGNATE 'HELLINGER.' SEARCH-PATTERN ESTABLISHED TO COMB ALL RELEVANT DATA AND...

SHUT UP, 'PUTER! *NOT NOW!!*

THEN *YOU* MUST BE THE *DOC!* THE ONE THAT *MADE* ME A WALKIN' *FREAK!*

WHY MUST I BE *ANYONE,* DEATHLOK? I'M MERELY *HELLINGER.*

I AM WHAT *I AM!*

EXCUSE ME A MOMENT WHILE I SWITCH OFF THE--ER-- 'OTHER' LUTHER MANNING IN THE STUDY!

THE *CLONE,* YOU MEAN! THAT THING OUT THERE *IS* A CLONE, ISN'T IT??

OF COURSE IT *IS!* WHAT *ELSE* WOULD IT BE?

THEN THEY *CLONED* ME BEFORE I *DIED*-- BEFORE THEY MADE ME A *MONSTER!*

THAT MEANS THERE'S A FORM *COMPATIBLE* WITH MY *BRAIN*--A FORM THAT WOULDN'T REJECT A *MIND-TRANSFER!*

NO, I'M AFRAID *NOT,* DEATHLOK.

THERE SIMPLY ISN'T ENOUGH OF THE FIRST LUTHER MANNING *LEFT* TO TRANSFER! ASK YOUR *COMPUTER* IF YOU DON'T *BELIEVE ME!*

SUBJECT IS CORRECT. REMAINING ORGANIC ELEMENTS OF CYBORG TOO FRAGMENTED TO ALLOW SUCCESSFUL IMPLANTATION IN NEW FORM.

OKAY, 'PUTER--I *BELIEVE* YOU! NOW WHAT DO I DO ABOUT *THIS* BIRD?

ALTHOUGH DATA IS NOT AVAILABLE ON SUBJECT-DESIGNATE 'HELLINGER'...PRELIMINARY ANALYSIS SUGGESTS SUBJECT IS NOT A TARGET...REPEAT ...SUBJECT IS NOT...

YEAH, NOT A *TARGET!* I GOT THE SAME *FEELIN'* ABOUT HIM, 'PUTER!

OKAY, BUSTER--YOU *LIVE*-- FOR THE TIME BEING!

THANK YOU. NOW PERHAPS I MIGHT SUGGEST A WAY WE TWO MIGHT WORK *TOGETHER!*

TALK, THEN-- I AIN'T GOIN' *NOWHERE!*

OMNI-COMPUTER READOUT. OPERATION
COMPLETED. INITIATE PROGRAMMING
FOR POST-OPERATIVE CARE.

THE COMPUTER'S TAKING *OVER* NOW, DOCTOR!

THE OPERATION IS *DONE!*

YES. WE'VE DONE WHAT WE WERE *FORCED* TO DO!

HE--HE'LL--

YES... HE'LL *LIVE*, DOCTOR.

CHECK THOSE *ELECTRODES* ONCE MORE, PLEASE.

NOTHING MUST DISTURB THE LINKAGE *NOW*, GENTLEMEN.

PHYSICAL STRUCTURE OF SUBJECT 'HELL-
INGER' BLURRED. CONSIDERABLE ORGAN-
IC SURGERY GRAFTED ONTO ORIGINAL
PHYSIOGNOMY.

HE AIN'T WHAT HE *PRETENDS* TO BE, HUH 'PUTER?

I AIN'T HEARD NUTHIN' *YET*, HELLINGER!

AND I KNOW WHY *YOU* ARE HERE-- BUT THERE IS *NO WAY* I CAN *HELP* YOU NOW!

WAIT! BEFORE YOU *SAY* ANYTHING--

--ALLOW ME TO *EXPLAIN!*

RADIATION POISONING, DEATHLOK!

MY *NERVOUS SYSTEM* IS SLOWLY *DETERIO- RATING!*

LEAVING ME PLAY- ING WITH *CLONES* FOR AMUSEMENT --TO PASS THE *TIME!*

HELLINGER REPORT. DATA CODE 104011. SUBJECT MIKE
TRAVERS LOCATED ON ROOFTOP NEAR PERIMETER OF NORTH
WALL. SUBJECT IS ARMED.

SEEMS *QUIET* DOWN THERE!

WHY HAVEN'T RYKER'S *GOONS* COME AFTER *US?*

AN' WHY DID I GO BACK FOR *NINA* IN THE FIRST PLACE?

OH, BUT YOU *HAVE,* DEATHLOK!

BY NOW YOUR COMPUTER HAS INFORMED YOU THAT I AM *NOT* IN ITS *DATA BANKS*--

--WHICH IS *IMPOSSIBLE* SINCE EVERY-ONE IS FILED NEATLY AWAY WITH-IN THE BRAIN OF THE *OMNI-COMPUTER!*

EVERYONE EXCEPT *ME,* THAT IS, THO' *THAT IS* MY LITTLE *SECRET!*

BUT I STILL HAVEN'T *THANKED* YOU FOR *FREEING ME!* YOU SEE--I *AM* THE SURGEON WHO OPERATED ON YOU--AND RYKER HAS *IMPRISONED* ME HERE EVER SINCE--

FROM HERE ON *IN* MAJOR RYKER IS IN THE HANDS OF THE *OMNI-COMPUTER!*

HE--*THEY*--ARE NOW *ONE* AND THE *SAME!*

POSSIBLY THE FIRST *HUMAN* EQUIVALENT TO A *GOD!*

THEN HE'S REACHED HIS *OBJECTIVE,* DOCTOR? HE'S SOLD HIS CHANCE AT *HUMANITY* FOR THE SOUL OF A *MACHINE.*

YES... HE'S *REACHED* HIS OBJECTIVE, GENTLEMEN.

WHAT ABOUT ALL THE *OTHERS?*

YOU COULDN'T HAVE OPERATED *ALONE!!*

NO...BUT THEY ARE SIMILARLY *AFFLICTED!*

RYKER *PLANNED IT* THAY WAY--AS A *PRECAUTION* FOR THE *FUTURE!*

BUT THERE *IS* A WAY WE CAN STRIKE *BACK* AT HIM, MY CYBORG FRIEND! *WATCH*--

MAJOR RYKER IS NOW THE *SAVIOR MACHINE*--

--AND MAY GOD HELP US *ALL.*

HELLINGER TERMINAL EYE READOUT #2. MINDLOCK SUBJECT NINA WITH SUBJECT TRAVERS...MINDLOCK COMPLETED PRIOR TO SUBJECT'S ABDUCTION FROM CYBERNETICS SECTION.

AH--AS I'D *HOPED!* I'M STILL *ALIVE!* WHICH LEADS ME TO *ASSUME* THAT I WILL *STAY* THAT WAY?

MAYBE...

FINE, *FINE!* MEANWHILE--IT *OCCURS* TO ME THAT PERHAPS YOU'VE BEEN *WONDERING* WHY-- IN THIS AGE OF APPARENT *BIOLOGICAL SUPER-SCIENCE*--

EVERYONE RYKER'S *THROWN* AT YOU--AS WELL AS THE *REVOLUTIONARIES* --IS ARMED WITH ARCHAIC *WEAPONRY!* THE *ANSWER* IS BEHIND THAT DOOR, DEATHLOK!

ANALYSIS OF DOOR: STEEL-REINFORCED OAK. READOUT OF STRESS FACTOR...

I'VE ALREADY FIGURED *OUT* WHAT IT'LL *TAKE* TO WASTE IT, 'PUTER!

SKRAM

NOTED AND FILED FOR FUTURE REFERENCE.

HOLY *CRUD!* LASERS! *FISSION GRENADES!* 'CUSSION BOMBS!

AND *MORE,* DEATHLOK! TAKE YOUR *PICK!* THEY ARE *ALL* FUNCTIONAL!

AS WELL AS A *SPECIALTY ITEM* I'M SAVING FOR RYKER!

I'VE SEEN A *LOT* OF HARDWARE IN MY TIME, HELLINGER--

--A LOT OF WAYS TO *KILL A MAN!*

SOME OF 'EM *RYKER* TAUGHT ME!

FIND A WAY TO MAKE ME *NORMAL,* HELLINGER!

AN' I'LL MAKE RYKER *PAY!* I *PROMISE* YOU!

TIME: 8:03 P.M. {I} {WE} {OMNI-COMPUTER-RYKER} READOUT ON LOCATION OF DEATHLOK/LUTHER MANNING/ CYBORG. SUBJECT HAS LEFT LONG ISLAND. ACTIVITIES NOT RECORDED...INTERFER-ENCE SUGGESTS...'HELL-INGER, COMPUTER! HE CREATED THAT INTERFERENCE!

AFFIRMATIVE. 'WHERE IS HE HEADED? {I} {WE} NEED A READOUT!' DESTINATION INCONCLUSIVE. 'FOLLOW, COMPUTER!' FOLLOWING.

HOPE YOU'RE KEEPIN' TRACK O' THE TIME, 'PUTER!

AFFIRMATIVE. 8:07 P.M.

THAT LEAVES ME TWENTY-THREE MINUTES TO DELIVER THIS LITTLE PACKAGE!

TWENTY-TWO. TIME: 8:08 P.M.

PRESENT ACTION ILLOGICAL. ATTACHE CASE CLAMPED TO WRIST BY SUBJECT-DESIGNATE HELLINGER CONTAINS BOMB CAPABLE OF DESTROYING THIS ENTITY.

I KNOW, 'PUTER!

BUT THE RISK IS MINIMAL COMPARED TO WHAT I STAND TO WIN!

A CHANCE TO ACE RYKER ONCE AND FOR ALL!

'SIDES, I CAN UNHITCH THIS BOMB WHENEVER I WANT--

NEGATIVE. DEVICE SET TO EXPLODE IMMEDIATELY IF TAMPERED WITH.

TIME: 8:10 P.M. DETONATION TIME: TWENTY MINUTES.

Y'KNOW, 'PUTER--OUR PROBLEM SEEMS TO BE THAT EVERYONE ELSE SEEMS TO KNOW WHAT I'VE GOT IN MIND BEFORE AND AFTER I DECIDE TO LET 'EM KNOW!

AFFIRMATIVE. LINK WITH OMNI-COMPUTER STILL FUNCTIONAL.

WHAT!? YOU TELL ME THAT NOW??

WHAT THE HELL! IT SORT OF FIGURED!

THIS IS THE WALL WHERE LINC SHAND GOT HIMSELF BLASTED TRYIN' TO FIGHT THAT TANK!*

*SEE ISSUE #30--MARV.

POOR DOPE! NOT MUCH LEFT OF HIM, THOUGH.

MEMORY-TAPES CLASS DATA AS IMMATERIAL...

DON'T ERASE 'EM, 'PUTER! THEY'RE MINE!

AN' I'M ENTITLED TO KEEP SOMETHIN'!

NOTED. TIME: 8:15 P.M.

WARNING. ATTACK.

KNEW I DIDN'T LIKE THE LOOKS OF THIS PARK!

TOO MANY TREES! TOO MANY PLACES TO HIDE!

DELAY MAY BE FATAL TO ORGANISM. FOURTEEN MINUTES TO DETONATION. REPEAT...

HELLINGER REPORT: CYBORG DESIGNATE 'DEATHLOK' HAS ALLOWED HIMSELF TO BE TAKEN BY PROVISIONAL REVOLUTIONARIES IN MANHATTAN SECTOR CP110-- CENTRAL PARK. TIME: 8:21 P.M. DETONATION TIME OF EXPLOSIVE IN ATTACHE CASE: NINE MINUTES.

"WHERE WE GOIN' TIN-SOLDIER?"

"SHUT UP, CYBORG-- AN' KEEP MOVIN'!"

PERFECT! ALL TOO PERFECT!

SOON, MY CLONE, DEATHLOK WILL REALIZE THAT THE 'SAFETY-MARGIN' I TOLD HIM WAS INCORPORATED INTO THE BOMB'S DESIGN--

--DOES NOT EXIST!

HE IS PLAYING MY GAME, NOW! MY WAY!

A GAME THAT UNFORTUNATELY, HE HAS OUTLIVED HIS USEFULNESS IN AS A PLAYER!

A ROLE YOU WILL SOON TAKE ON, MY CLONE!

THE PLASTIC 'HANDS' I USED TO ESTABLISH MY TALE OF 'RADIATION POISONING' ARE NO LONGER NEEDED--

--AS USELESS AS THIS DISGUISE OF NORMALCY!

DISGUISE, MY CREATION--

--A GROSS DISTORTION OF MY TRUE SELF--

A SELF THAT NEEDS NO LONGER HIDE!

AS MY BROTHER --SIMON RYKER-- WILL SOON DISCOVER!

WHEN HE LOOKS AGAIN INTO MY EYES-- THE EYES THAT ARE THE PROTO-TYPE FOR THE NEW MAN-- THE HOMO-ASCENDANT!

MORE MACHINE THAN MAN!

TIME: 8:25 P.M. DETONATION TIME: FIVE MINUTES. DANGER... REPEAT...DANGER...

I'M JUST A MESSENGER IN THIS CRUMMY LITTLE WAR, FROM A DUDE NAME O' HELLINGER!

NEVER HEARD THE NAME, CYBORG!

FUNNY--HE SAID YOU'D KNOW IT! HE SAID A LOT OF THINGS, THO'.

Y'KNOW--I FEEL LIKE I'VE BEEN HAD, 'PUTER! LIKE ALL ALONG WE BEEN FIGHTING THE WRONG WAR--A KIND OF HOPELESS GUT-STINKIN' PUPPET WAR!

LISTEN TO THE FREAK, MAN! YOU TRYIN' TO COP THE VOTE FOR BEST ORATOR OF 1990, BRO'?

DETONATION TIME: ONE MIN-
UTE AND COUNTING...50 SEC-
ONDS AND COUNTING...DANGER
...DANGER...

JUST TRYIN'
TO SAY
WE'RE ALL
IN THIS
TOGETHER,
FRIEND!

NOT WHILE
YOU'RE TOTIN'
THE MONEY,
'FRIEND'!

I GOT NEWS
FOR YOU,
'FRIEND'.

THERE
AIN'T NO
MONEY!

CRACK!

LOOK OUT!
HE'S UP TO
SOMETHING!

...40 SECONDS...DANGER...
DANGER...

GOT TO KEEP 'EM OFF!
HELLINGER TOLD ME THIS
CABLE WOULD RELEASE IT-
SELF FROM MY WRIST
AT TEN SECONDS!

30 SECONDS TO DET-
ONATION...DANGER...

WHICH DON'T
LEAVE ME MUCH
TIME TO DELIVER
IT, DOES IT,
'PUTER!

GOTTA SCATTER
THESE BIRDS--GET
'EM OFF MY BACK--

--WITHOUT HURTIN'
'EM, 'CAUSE--LIKE
IT OR NOT--

TZATT!

I'M BEGINNIN'
TO DIG THAT WE
REALLY ARE ON THE
SAME SIDE!

AN' THERE'S THE
CASTLE! JUST WHERE
HELLINGER SAID
IT'D BE!

THAT'S WHERE
THEY'RE HOLDIN'
MIKE AN'
NINA!

HEY!
THE
CABLE!

IT'S
STILL ON!
IT HASN'T
RE-
LEASED!

DANGER: TIME-ELAPSE MECH-
ANISM FAILING TO RESPOND...
REPEAT...

8 SECONDS...
7...6...5...
4...3...

THAT DIRTY, DOUBLE-
CROSSIN' SON OF A--

--IT'S GONNA
BLOW ANY
SECOND,
'PUTER!

AN' US
WITH IT.!!

NEXT: "THE DOOMSDAY-MECHS!"

ASTONISHING TALES
MARVEL COMICS GROUP
APPROVED BY THE COMICS CODE AUTHORITY
25¢
34 MAR 02488
ASTONISHING TALES FEATURING
DEATHLOK THE DEMOLISHER!
ONLY DEATHLOK KNOWS THE ASTONISHING ANSWER--
WHAT HAPPENS WHEN A MAN BECOMES A MACHINE WITH THE POWER TO DESTROY THE EARTH?
BUT HE MAY NOT LIVE LONG ENOUGH TO TELL!
BUCKLER & JANSON '75
THE MAN WHO CONTROLLED THE WORLD!

A man locked in DEATH, No—not a MAN—a mockery of a man, an amalgam of flesh and computer-circuitry. that is the cyborg-designate DEATHLOK. Luther Manning has died and now, RESURRECTED in the year 1990, he searches with the fragment of humanity LEFT in him for a way to save both HIMSELF and his very SANITY.

Stan Lee PRESENTS: **DEATHLOK** THE DEMOLISHER! ™

'AND ALL THE KING'S MADMEN...

PRODUCED BY
RICH BUCKLER

SCRIPT: BILL MANTLO
CONCEPT, PLOT & ART:
RICH BUCKLER
INKS & COLORS: KLAUS JANSON
LETTERS: KAREN MANTLO
EDITING: MARV WOLFMAN

GOTTA TRY AN' **SCATTER** THESE DUDES WITHOUT **HURTIN'** 'EM, 'PUTER--

HELLINGER TERMINAL EYE READOUT: CYBORG-DESIGNATE DEATHLOK ENCOUNTERING RESISTANCE IN N.Y. SECTOR KNOWN AS CENTRAL PARK FROM GROUP KNOWN AS THE PROVISIONAL REVOLUTIONARY ARMY... FOLLOWING...

"...COULDN'T PUT DEATHLOK BACK TOGETHER AGAIN..."

--'CAUSE I'M JUST BEGINNING TO **DIG** THAT WE'RE ALL ON THE SAME **SIDE** IN THIS GUT-STINKIN', CRUMMY LITTLE WAR!

"...OR COULD THEY?"

...DANGER...DANGER...DETONATION TIME OF EXPLOSIVE WITHIN ATTACHE CASE CHAINED TO WRIST OF THIS ENTITY AT TWENTY SECONDS AND COUNTING... 19...

[149]

...18...

I HEAR YOU, 'PUTER! I'M DOIN' THE BEST I CAN!

BUT I GOTTA GET THROUGH THESE GUYS IN ORDER TO GET TO THE CASTLE... WHERE HELLINGER SAYS THEY'RE HOLDIN' MIKE--*

*SEE LAST ISSUE--MARV.

--AN' I GOTTA TRY AN' DO IT WITHOUT HURTIN' ANY OF 'EM!

HELLINGER TERMINAL-EYE READOUT: CYBORG-DESIGNATE DEATHLOK STILL BEARING EXPLOSIVE, LASER-FIRE SCATTERING FREE REVOLUTIONARIES.

...17 SECONDS AND COUNTING...

ALL RIGHT, 'PUTER--

...16... --I'M HURRYING! ...15...

--I'M HURRYING! ...14... ...13...

...12 SECONDS TO DETONATION...

THE CASTLE!

HELLINGER READOUT... DEATHLOK HAS REACHED DESTINATION... BELVEDERE CASTLE... FOLLOWING...

...11 SECONDS... HEY! THE CABLE ISN'T RELEASING!

IT'S SUPPOSED TO UNLOCK WHEN I REACH THE TARGET--

--SO I CAN DELIVER THE PAY-OFF AND SCRAM BEFORE--

HELLINGER!!

...10 SECONDS...

"AMUSING, ISN'T IT, DEATHLOK? THERE MUST BE A, AH... FAULTY-WIRE... SOMEWHERE!"

DAY-LOG: 1-1-91
TRAVERS REPORT

HAPPY *NEW YEAR*, LUTH'.

YOU MAY NOT *BELIEVE* THIS, LUTH'... EVEN IF YOU COULD *HEAR* ME--

--BUT I HOPE YOU'RE *ALIVE!*

HAVE REACHED LOCATION OF DEATHLOK-CYBORG, LIFTING HIM WITH SUPPLEMENTAL POWER OF EXO-SKELETON.

CYBORG APPEARS TO BE FUNCTIONALLY INACTIVE.

TROOM!

CHARGES SET AND DETONATED...

...CASTLE STRONGHOLD OF PROVISIONAL REVOLUTIONARY ARMY RENDERED INOPERATIVE.

I KNOW YOU SAID YOU'D *KILL ME* IF YOU EVER SAW ME AGAIN, LUTHER... FOR TAKING YOUR WIFE AND KID WHILE YOU WERE... *DEAD!*

BUT I DIDN'T DO ANY OF IT TO *HURT YOU*, LUTH'.

I HOPE YOU CAN *UNDERSTAND THAT!*

BA-WHOOM!

HELLINGER TERMINAL EYE READOUT: SENSORS INDICATE THAT OMNI-COMPUTER SENSING EYES HAVE BEEN EXPUNGED IN PARK SECTOR. CYBORG-BODY IS BEING RETRIEVED BY SUBJECT-DESIGNATE... TRAVERS.

"*FOLLOW, COMPUTER! I WANT TO KNOW WHERE TRAVERS TAKES THE, AH, BODY!*"

FOLLOWING...

DAY-LOG; 1-3-91. DEATHLOK'S BIONIC ARM HAS BEEN *RESTORED.*

REPLENISHMENT OF HIS DEPLETED *AMNIO-BIOTIC LIFE-FLUIDS* IS COMPLETE!

YOU'RE *WHOLE* AGAIN, LUTHER!

WHOLE! WE'RE GOING TO WAKE HIM *UP,* TRAVERS!

THE *BOSS* WANTS YOU TO BE HERE.

YEAH.

WASN'T *EASY* RESTORING THIS THING! LOOKED LIKE HE'D BEEN THROUGH A *WAR!*

HE *HAD!*

YEAH, WELL ... HE'S *BACK TOGETHER* AGAIN, *NOW!*

TOOK ALL THE KING'S *MADMEN* TO DO IT, HUH?

LOOK, TRAVERS--

ALL RIGHT! FORGET IT! HE'S *AWAKE!*

'PUTER! AM I--ARE WE--?

ALL SYSTEMS FUNCTIONING AT 100% CAPACITY. DECAY-FACTOR STABILIZED.

LUTHER--?

WE'RE ALIVE!

NEGATIVE, BUT WE EXIST.

GIVE HIM A *CHANCE,* MR. TRAVERS!

AFTER *ALL* ... IT'S NOT *EVERY DAY* ONE IS ALLOWED TO BE *RESURRECTED!*

'PUTER, I ... I CAN'T MOVE!

OUTSIDE PROGRAMING IN OPERATION. WE HAVE BEEN IMMOBILIZED.

I'M *SORRY* ABOUT THAT MR. MANNING--

--BUT UNTIL I'M *SURE* OF HOW YOU'LL *REACT* I'M AFRAID OUR PRECAUTION IS ... *NECESSARY!*

MY NAME IS *TERESA DEVEREAUX,* MR. MANNING ... AND YOU ARE IN THE HEADQUARTERS OF THE *CENTRAL INTELLIGENCE AGENCY*--

--OF WHICH I AM THE *HEAD!*

I THINK WE CAN ALLOW HIM *MOVEMENT* NOW, GENTLEMEN!

FULL MOBILITY RESTORED.

YOU ARE *OURS* NOW, DEATHLOK!

ANY *PREVIOUS* PROGRAMING HAS HAS BEEN *OVER-RIDDEN!*

IF YOU WILL GLANCE DOWN AT YOUR *RIGHT ARM,* YOU WILL NOTICE A *NEW INPUT TERMINAL!*

ALTHOUGH YOU MAY STILL FUNCTION AS AN *INDEPENDENT OPERATIVE--* OUR GOALS ARE *YOURS--* FOR THE TIME BEING!

'PUTER?

COMPUTER CHECK CORROBORATES AURAL INPUT. WE ARE NOW "PROGRAMED."

MR. TRAVERS WILL *EXPLAIN* IT ALL TO YOU, MR. MANNING.

EXPLAIN IT, TRAVERS!

TELL ME I'M A FREAKIN' *SUPER-SOLDIER,* A *DEATH-MACHINE* FOR *HIRE* AGAIN! A *COMPUTER JUNKIE!*

FIRST *RYKER!* NOW THE *CIA!* AN' *YOU* LET 'EM *DO IT* TO ME!

NOBODY'S DOING *ANYTHING* TO YOU, LUTH'.

NOBODY EXCEPT *RYKER!*

AN' YOU'RE GONNA TELL ME THAT RYKER DON'T *OWN* THE CIA?

HE'S THE *GOVERNMENT,* TRAVERS! HE'S *GOD* IF HE WANTS TO BE!

HE MAY ALREADY BE *BOTH,* LUTH'--

THAT'S THE *REASON* FOR ALL OF THIS!

THE CIA THINKS THAT *YOU* ARE THE ONLY CHANCE OF *STOPPING RYKER!* HE *BUILT* YOU! MADE YOU MORE *POWERFUL* THAN ANYBODY REALLY *KNOWS!*

THEY'RE *FIGHTING HIM,* LUTH'--AND WE'VE GOT TO *HELP THEM!*

YOU'RE A *LIAR,* TRAVERS!

BUT YOU'RE NOT GOING TO LIE *ANYMORE!*

NO USE, LUTH'! YOU'RE *PROGRAMMED,* REMEMBER! YOU *CAN'T* SHOOT ME!

ANALYSIS CORRECT. ACTION IS CONTRARY TO PROGRAMING.

YOUR POWER HAS TO BE USED AGAINST *RYKER,* LUTH'--

--BUT NOT *BLINDLY,* THE WAY YOU'VE *BEEN* USING IT!

BELIEVE ME, IT'S FOR THE *BEST!*

HE'S TELLING THE *TRUTH*, MR. MANNING!

YEAH?

I SUPPOSE ALL THE *HARDWARE* IS TO MAKE SURE I *AGREE!*

WE'VE BEEN *CAGED* FOR A LONG TIME, MR. MANNING-- AND WE WANT *OUT!*

I'M AFRAID *SO!* THE GIRL *NINA*--WHOM RYKER HAD TURNED INTO AN *OMNI-COMPUTER TERMINAL OUTLET* HAS PROBED THE MAIN COMPUTER BANKS--

*SEE ISH #28--MARV.

I'M *SURE* YOU CAN *UNDERSTAND THAT!*

-- AND EVEN AS WE *SPEAK*, THE MAJOR IS WELL ON HIS WAY TO BECOMING *OMNIPOTENT!* WE *NEED YOU* DEATHLOK!

NO! THEY'RE JUST FOLLOWING PROCE- DURE. CALL IT *INSURANCE!*

GUIDE THE 'COPTER IN *SLOW*, 'PUTER! I WANT RYKER'S *GOONS* TO GET A GOOD, *HARD* LOOK AT IT!

AFFIRMATIVE.

HELICOPTER APPROACHING TARGET.

HERE HE *COMES*, BOYS-- JUST LIKE THE *OMNI-COMP* SAID!

THAT *CYBORG* MUST BE MORE *RECKLESS* THAN WE WERE *TOLD...* CHARGIN' IN HERE IN *BROAD DAYLIGHT!*

-- THIS IS WHERE HE *BUYS* IT!

BUT *DUMB* AS THAT IS--

OPEN FIRE!

SENSORS INDICATE VEHICLE UNDER ATTACK BY CONCENTRATED LASER-FIRE.

[156]

--TWO LEFT TO GO!

GET HI--!

STRAMMMM!

LOOKS LIKE *YOU TWO* DON'T NEED *MY HELP* IN GETTIN' *ZAPPED!*

WHAT-- WHAT'RE YOU GONNA *DO?*

NOT MUCH, CRUD--

-- JUST GET YOU OUTTA MY *WAY*--

SMASH!

--SO I CAN HAVE ME A LITTLE *TALK* WITH YOUR *PARTNER!*

NO! D-DON'T HIT ME!

PLEASE!

JUST TELL ME WHERE *RYKER* IS--

-- AND WE'LL *BOTH* WALK AWAY FROM HERE *ALIVE!*

SURE I'LL TELL YOU! WHY *NOT?* HE'S DOWN *THERE* ... THROUGH THAT *DOOR!*

FIGHT IT OUT WITH *HIM!* I'M JUST A *FLUNKY,* A *PATSY,* CYBORG--

--JUST LIKE *YOU!*

I SHOULD HAVE *SHOT HIM,* 'PUTER!

IRRATIONAL. HIS STATE-MENTS WERE CORRECT.

THAT'S WHAT I *MEAN!*

CALCULATIONS INDICATE PROBABLE LOCATION OF MAIN OMNI-COMPUTER BANK BEHIND DOOR.

'AN WHERE HIS *TOYS* ARE--

--THAT'S *GENERALLY* WHERE *RYKER* IS!

HOPE YOU'RE *EXPECTIN'* ME, MAJOR--

-- CAUSE I'M *COMIN' IN!*

AN' THIS *TIME* THERE AIN'T *NUTHIN'* GONNA STOP ME--

WE'RE SEEING THIS THROUGH *DEATHLOK'S* EYES?

YES, MS. DEVEREAUX!

THAT'S ONE OF THE LITTLE... *IMPROVEMENTS* WE ADDED TO THE CYBORG WHEN WE *REBUILT* HIM!

THEN MAJOR RYKER IS *ALREADY* LINKED WITH THE OMNI-COMPUTER!

DOES MANNING STAND A CHANCE, COINES?

YES, MA'AM... BUT NOT A VERY *BIG ONE!*

THE OVER-RIDE PROGRAMMING WE INCORPORATED INTO HIS *SYSTEM* MUST HAVE HIM FEELING LIKE AN *ADDICT* ABOUT NOW!

HE'LL *FACE* ANYTHING... *DO* ANYTHING TO GET TO RYKER AND THUS SATISFY HIS *NEED!*

I WISH THERE WAS SOME *OTHER WAY!*

"--BUT IF RYKER *SUCCEEDS*... WELL, DEATHLOK'S *AFFLICTION* WILL BE THE *LEAST* OF OUR WORRIES!"

GOT... TO... *SHUT*... *DOWN* THE ...DEFENSE ...SYSTEM...

...STOP...THE ...SOUND....

IT'S DONE!

THANK *GOD!*

RETURN TO PRO-GRAMMED ACTION.

GET RYKER.

RYKER!

GET ME *READY*, DOC!

FAST!

I CAN'T *HELP MYSELF*, DOC! MY PROGRAMMING SAY'S *"GET RYKER"*--

-- AND I GOT TO *JUMP!*

AND ANYBODY WHO SEEMS TO BE IN MY *WAY* GETS IT!

PROGRAMMING? ALL RIGHT THEN... *NEGATE* YOUR PROGRAMMING BY LETTING IT KNOW THAT IF YOU KILL *ME*--

-- YOU'LL *NEVER* GET IN AFTER THE *MAJOR!*

I'M THE *ONLY ONE* WHO CAN PERFORM THE *LINKAGE!*

THAT *DID IT,* DOC!

PUTER...?

PROGRAMMING DOES NOT CONTRADICT. PROCEED.

LINK ME, DOC!

HELLINGER TERMINAL EYE READOUT: SUBJECT-DESIGNATE "RYKER" IS MIND-LOCKED TO TOTAL-FUNCTIONING OF THE OMNI-COMPUTER. SUJECT-DESIGNATE "DEATHLOK" PREPARING FOR INTERCEPT-LINKAGE.

GOING IN *AFTER* SIMON, DEATHLOK?

GOOD! *GOOD!* BETTER THEN EVEN *I* COULD HAVE *PLANNED!*

COME, MY CLONE! COME OUT!

I WISH YOUR UNCOMPREHENDING *EYES* TO *WITNESS THIS!*

THE *DESTRUCTION* OF EVERY-THING MY SAINTED *BROTHER* HAS WORKED FOR--

-- THE *END* OF HIS *BENEVOLENT TECHNOLOGY* AT THE HANDS OF HIS *GREATEST TECHNOLOGICAL CREATION!*

AND ONCE BOTH SIMON *AND* DEATHLOK ARE OUT OF THE *WAY*--

THEN THE WORLD WILL *SCREAM* BEFORE YOU, MY CLONE--

-- THE *FIRST* OF THE *DOOMSDAY-MECHS!*

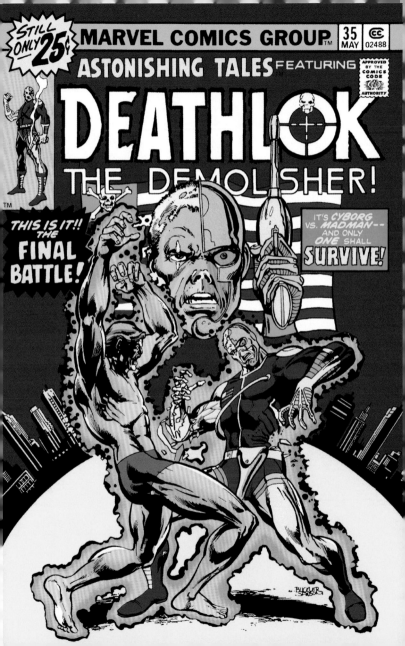

A man locked in DEATH, No—not a MAN—a mockery of a man, an amalgam of flesh and computer-circuitry that is the cyborg-designate DEATHLOK. Luther Manning has died and now, RESURRECTED in the year 1990, he searches with the fragment of humanity LEFT in him for a way to save both HIMSELF and his very SANITY.
Stan Lee PRESENTS: DEATHLOK THE DEMOLISHER! TM
...and once removed from NEVER
THIS...IS... INSANE, 'PUTER! ONE MINUTE THERE'S A BIG LAUGHIN' FACE OF RYKER LOOKIN' DOWN AT ME--
--THE NEXT I'M IN FREE-FALL, ROLLIN' THROUGH THE STARS LIKE A LIVIN' PIN-BALL!
WHERE ARE WE, 'PUTER?
WHAT'S HAPPENING?
AN' HOW DO WE STOP IT?!
PRODUCED BY: RICH BUCKLER
CONCEPT, PLOT & ART: RICH BUCKLER
SCRIPT: BILL MANTLO
INKS & COLORS: KLAUS JANSON
LETTERING: KAREN MANTLO
MARV WOLFMAN EDITOR
JV 215

SYSTEMS-CHECK·ESTABLISHES THAT TOTAL MIND-LOCK SUC-
CESSFULLY EFFECTED...WE ARE NOW INSIDE THE OMNI-
COMPUTER AS A RANDOM FREQUENCY SCANNING-WAVE...
TRACKING AT A RATE OF ·3 CYCLES PER MILLISECOND...

I'M NOT *REAL*??

ALL RIGHT, THEN... NEITHER IS *RYKER!*

LIGHT??

I'M JUST A *LIGHT-BEAM?*

LOCK ON TO HIM, 'PUTER!

HE'S WHAT I CAME *IN* HERE FOR!!

JUST GET ME *RYKER!!*

WELCOME, DEATHLOK.

YOU FLOW WITHIN THE MATRIX OF {MY} {OUR} BEING.

THE FACE, 'PUTER! IT'S *BACK* AGAIN!

PHOTONS ARRANGED IN 'SENSE-PATTERN'
TRANSLATION FOR OUR BENEFIT ONLY...

...VISUALS NOT 'REAL' ...REPEAT...

GLAD TO *HEAR IT*, MAJOR--

'CAUSE IT MEANS I DON'T HAVE TO FIGURE OUT ANY FANCY *NEW* WAYS OF *KILLIN'* YOU!

A GOOD OLD-FASHIONED *LASER-BLAST* WILL DO IT !!

WILL IT, DEATHLOK?

{MINE} IS THE OVER-RIDING SIGNAL-IMPULSE WITHIN THE 'BRAIN' OF THE OMNI-COM-PUTER...AND {I} CAN DE-STROY YOU...

...AS EASILY AS {I} NEGATE THE 'ILLUSION' THAT IS YOUR WEAPON.

SHATTERED...??

NEGATIVE. MOLECULAR PATTERN DISRUPTED.

CORRECT, COMPUTER! AND DONE AS EASILY AS THE CREATION OF THIS PHOTONIC EARTH!

A SIMPLE REARRANGEMENT OF LIGHT SO THAT I MAY SHOW YOU, DEATHLOK, THE WORLD YOU MISSED WHILE THE BODY AND MIND OF LUTHER MANNING LAY DEAD FOR FIVE YEARS!

THE SAME WORLD YOU TURNED INTO A NIGHTMARE, RYKER?

NO, DEATHLOK! A NIGHTMARE I AM GOING TO RE-STRUCTURE AS A PARADISE!

FOLLOW ME, DEATHLOK! DOWN TO EARTH, 1985!

DO I HAVE ANY CHOICE?

NOT REALLY!

I HAVE BOUND YOUR ELECTRONS TO MY MOLECULAR STRUCTURE.

FOR NOW, AT LEAST--

--WE ARE ONE!

LIKE YOU SAID, MAJOR--

--FOR NOW!!

--AND CHAOS!

LOOK *BELOW*... AT *LONG ISLAND!*

YOU *MOVED* EVERYONE IN *MANHATTAN?*

IT WAS *ESSENTIAL!* THE ENEMY HAD DISRUPTED DAY-TO-DAY *FUNCTIONING!*

WE HAD NO OTHER *CHOICE!*

BULL! THERE *WAS* NO ENEMY, RYKER!

YOU JUST WANTED *CONTROL*... TOTAL, COMPLETE *ORDER!*

AND THE ONLY WAY TO *GET IT* WAS TO GET RID OF THE *CAUSES OF DISORDER:*

GAZE UPON A NEW *METROPOLIS,* POPULATED BY THE PEOPLE WE *EVACUATED* FROM NEW YORK CITY AFTER THE *DISRUPTION!*

PEOPLE, RYKER! PEOPLE CAUSE DISORDER!

SO YOU GOT RID OF THE *PEOPLE!*

ROUNDED 'EM UP AN' *HERDED* 'EM OUT TO LONG ISLAND... INTO A CITY THAT'S REALLY A *MILITARY COMPLEX* ...SO YOU COULD KEEP YOUR DAMNED COMPUTER *EYES* ON 'EM--

--ALL FOR THE SAKE OF *ORDER!!*

THEY WENT *WILLINGLY,* DEATHLOK--

--ONCE THEY WERE MADE TO *SEE!*

SEE *WHAT??*

THAT IT WAS FOR THEIR OWN *GOOD!* PEOPLE *NEED* SOMEONE TO WATCH *OVER* THEM!

SO YOU ELECTED *YOURSELF!*

DICTATOR AND *GOD* ALL ROLLED INTO *ONE!*

YOU'RE *MAD* RYKER!

YOU'RE *INSANE!!*

FLOW *REVERSED*, DR. WILCOX!

BOTH BODIES ARE *DORMANT*!

ALL RIGHT, DOCTOR. WE'LL TRY *AGAIN*!

AND *THIS* TIME--

-- LET'S GET IT *RIGHT*!

AARRRGGGHHH!!

THE ... PAIN ...

... HANDS ... *STRANGE* ... METAL ... COIL ... ?

I CAN'T HEAR MY *HEART-BEAT*...

... *NOT ALIVE!*

I -- I'M *DEATHLOK*!!

I'M DEAD--

-- I'M A *CYBORG* AND I'M *DEAD*!!!

HE -- HE'S GONE COMPLETELY *MAD*! RAVING LIKE A *LUNATIC*!

IT WAS THE *TRANSFERENCE*--! HE STILL THINKS HE'S THE *CYBORG*!

AND HE'S JUST *LEARNED* WHAT IT MEANS TO BE A WALKING "*PATCHWORK-MAN*"--

--SHARING HIS "*LIFE*" WITH THE COLD CIRCUITRY OF A *COMPUTER*!

MAY THE LORD *HELP* HIM!

WE'RE *BACK*, 'PUTER!

AFFIRMATIVE.

COLD METAL *HALF-HANDS* REACHING FOR ME!

TRYING TO *TAKE* MY MIND *AWAY*!

KEEP THEM *BACK*!

DON'T *HURT* ME, DEATHLOK!

I -- I DIDN'T ... *DO* ANYTHING! I--

--I DIDN'T *WANT* IT TO BE *THIS* WAY!

-- NOT LIKE -- THIS!

HELLINGER TERMINAL-EYE READ-OUT: ENTITY-DESIGNATE 'SIMON RYKER' HAS BEEN NEUTRAL-
IZED...FUNCTIONING OF MASTER COMPUTER DISRUPTED...REPAIR SYSTEMS SHUT DOWN...SUB-
JECT DESIGNATES 'DEATHLOK' AND 'WILCOX' STILL FUNCTIONING AND STILL IN CONTROL...

CONTROL? CONTROL OF *WHAT*??

I SUPPOSE I SHOULD *MOURN* YOU, MY DEAR BROTHER *SIMON*--

-- BUT, YOU SEE, I HAVEN'T THE *TIME!*

THE MANNING-CLONE IS *READY*... THE *RADIATION-BATH* IS COMPLETE--

-- AND EVEN AS YOU LIE BROKEN AND *GROVELLING* IN YOUR *MADNESS*, SIMON--

-- THE *FIRST* OF THE *DOOMSDAY-MECHS* STEPS *FORTH!!*

YOUR PRECIOUS AGE OF *"ORDER"* IS DONE, MY BROTHER!

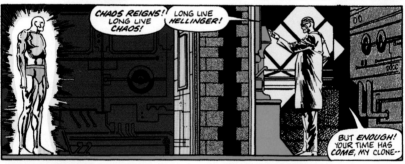

CHAOS REIGNS! LONG LIVE CHAOS!

LONG LIVE *HELLINGER!*

BUT *ENOUGH!* YOUR TIME HAS *COME*, MY CLONE--

"-- TO STEP OUT FROM BEHIND THIS THICKNESS OF *LEAD-SHIELDING* --

"-- AND GO FORTH INTO THE *WORLD!* A *NEW* WORLD!

"*OUR WORLD*...WHERE, AS YOUR RADIOACTIVE MASS SLOWLY *DETERIORATES* --

"-- YOU WILL GATHER UNTO *YOURSELF* THE FORCE OF THE *MILLENIUM*:

"THE DESTRUCTIVE POWER OF THE *PORTABLE PLUTONIUM BOMB!!*"

...END CHAPTER ONE.

2 THE RESURRECTION AND THE DEATH!

YOU'RE A REGULAR *ONE-MAN ARMY*, DEATHLOK! VERY WELL DONE. IF I MAY *CONGRATULATE* YOU...

STOW IT, LADY! IT'S WHAT YOUR BOYS *PROGRAMMED ME* TO DO, RIGHT?

BUT I GOT ONE REAL *PROBLEM*. IF I WAS SUPPOSED TO FINISH RYKER, WHATTA I DO NOW WHEN EVERY QUIVERING INCH OF MY *CIRCUITRY* TELLS ME I *CAN'T* QUIT--

--BECAUSE RYKER IS NOT *DEAD?* THE ANSWER IS SIMPLE...

...WE ALTERED THE CODING OF YOUR *PRIME DIRECTIVE* SO THAT YOU *BELIEVED* THAT.

YOU WERE CONVINCED THAT ALL YOU *EXISTED* FOR WAS TO DESTROY RYKER. BUT HE *HAS* BEEN TERMINATED --AS A *THREAT.*

THEN, THERE'S NUTHIN' TO *PREVENT* ME ...

...FROM GETTIN' RID OF THIS *TERMINAL* HERE ...

...THAT KEEPS SENDING SIGNALS TO *MESS OVER* MY *MIND!*

AN' THAT MEANS *I'M* FINISHED, TOO, LADY! YOU CAN TAKE YOUR CRUMMY READY-MADE *DICTUMS*--

-- AN' *STUFF* 'EM!

'CAUSE I'VE HAD *ALL ... I ... CAN TAKE!*

YOU PEOPLE OUGHTTA BE *REAL PROUD*...

YOU CAN SHOVE A *WIRE* IN ANYBODY'S BRAIN, NOW--

--AN' HAVE THE *WHOLE FREAKIN' WORLD* FOR YOUR OWN PRIVATE PUPPET SHOW!

BUT *COUNT ME OUT!!*

DEATHLOK! YOU DON'T JUST WALK OUT OF THIS WITH YOUR HANDS *UNSOILED*...

IT'S *STILL RYKER'S WORLD* OUT THERE. THERE'S *WORK* TO BE DONE.

SURE, SURE. AND I'M THE *WORK HORSE*, RIGHT? I GET THE DIRTY END OF IT. STILL... *N-O*.

THERE'S MORE. YOU REMEMBER *NINA*, THE WOMAN RYKER WIRED TO HIS *OMNI-COMPUTER*? SHE'S SUPPLIED US WITH *NEW INFORMATION*!

SO. SHE'S *NOTHING* TO ME.

MAYBE. BUT WE HAVE *PROOF*-- THERE IS A THREAT EVEN *MORE* SERIOUS--

RYKER'S *BROTHER*, DEATHLOK! *HELLINGER*!

SUBJECT: HELLINGER. NO AVAILABLE DATA. ACTIONS IN PAST SEVENTY TWO HRS INDICATE HELLINGER IS A THREAT. LOGICAL ACTION...

I KNOW WHAT THE LOGICAL ACTION SHOULD BE. THIS *JERK* ALMOST GOT ME *KILLED* WHEN I DELIVERED HIS LITTLE PACKAGE THAT *BLEW* UP THE P.R.A.

OKAY, I GOT MY OWN REASONS. I'M STICKING *WITH IT*, FOR *NOW*.

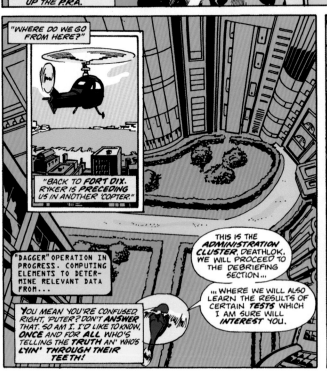

"WHERE DO WE GO FROM HERE?"

"BACK TO *FORT DIX*. RYKER IS *PRECEDING* US IN ANOTHER 'COPTER."

"DAGGER" OPERATION IN PROGRESS. COMPUTING ELEMENTS TO DETER- MINE RELEVANT DATA FROM...

YOU MEAN YOU'RE CONFUSED, RIGHT, 'PUTER? DON'T *ANSWER* THAT. SO AM I. I'D LIKE TO KNOW, *ONCE* AND FOR ALL WHO'S TELLING THE *TRUTH* AN' WHO'S *LYIN'* THROUGH THEIR *TEETH*!

THIS IS THE *ADMINISTRATION CLUSTER*, DEATHLOK. WE WILL PROCEED TO THE DEBRIEFING SECTION...

... WHERE WE WILL ALSO LEARN THE RESULTS OF CERTAIN *TESTS* WHICH I AM SURE WILL *INTEREST* YOU.

THE ONLY THING I'M INTERESTED IN IS *RUNNING FROM MYSELF*, LADY!

ANYTHING ELSE IS *JUST BIDING TIME*!

I UNDERSTAND... MORE THAN YOU *THINK*!

READ-OUT: HAVE COMPENSATED FOR ADDITIONAL WEIGHT OF CYBORG FORM. LANDING COMPLETE. AN AREA SCAN REVEALS...

--*THAT* WE'RE NOT IN THE *DEBRIEFING SECTION.* I SORTA *NOTICED* THE SAME THING, 'PUTER.

THIS WAY. WE HAVE TO PASS THE *CRYOGENICS* SECTION ON OUR WAY. SECURITY THERE IS *TOP-LEVEL*--

--SO WE CAN SPEAK *FREELY.*

SOLDIERS ALL OVER THE FREAKIN' PLACE. THE STENCH OF *CARBINE-OIL* IS STRONG ENOUGH TO MAKE ME *PUKE.*

ILLOGICAL. SENSE OF SMELL NOT A CYBERNETIC FUNCTION OF THIS UNIT. SENSORY ANALYSIS...

I HEARD IT ALL BEFORE. YOUR *CIRCUITS* WERE RATTLIN' AWAY EVEN BACK WHEN WE HADDA *BUST* OUR WAY OUT OF HERE!

EVERYTHING WAS CONFUSING, MADDENING-- ESPECIALLY THE *GUNFIRE* COMIN' FROM THE RIFLES OF MEN I HAD *SERVED* WITH...

IT-- IT'S RYKER'S *CYBORG!*

HE'S GONE *BERSERK!*

FROM CYBORG *RUN AMOK* TO COOL, SMOOTH-AS-POLISHED-STEEL *MURDER-MACHINE*-- WE'VE COME A LONG-WAY, EH 'PUTER?

THESE CORRIDORS LEAD TO *SURGICAL OPERATIONS.*

-- THERE IS *SOMETHING* I THINK YOU SHOULD *KNOW,* DEATHLOK...

LIKE, THAT I'VE BEEN *SET UP,* LADY? AWRIGHT, WHO'S *BEHIND* THE *DOOR?*

YOU DON'T TRUST *ANY-ONE,* DO YOU? I... I CAN'T REALLY *BLAME* YOU FOR THAT...

"AS FOR WHAT LIES AHEAD -- IF I *REALLY* INTENDED TO HAVE YOU *KILLED,* IT COULD HAVE BEEN DONE A *DOZEN* TIMES ALREADY."

"I'M AFRAID IT DOESN'T BREAK DOWN TO ANYTHING QUITE THAT *SIMPLE.* YOU'RE BEING BRIEFED ON A *NEED-TO-KNOW* BASIS-- STANDARD FOR C.I.A. OPERATIONS."

"LIKE FOR EXAMPLE: THE FLOOR BENEATH YOUR FEET IS *PRESSURE-SENSITIVE.* IF ANY OTHER THAN WE *TWO*-- ANY MORE, OR LESS --HAD ATTEMPTED TO *TRA-VERSE* THESE HALLS--"

"--THEY WOULD HAVE BEEN *VAPORIZED* IN SECONDS!"

SENSORY DATA: NO VISUAL THREAT PRESENT.

YEAH, BUT ANYTHING COULD BE *HIDIN'* BEHIND THESE WALLS.

WHAT IN HOLY--?

I *WANTED* TO TELL YOU, DEATHLOK--BUT I KNEW YOU WOULDN'T *BELIEVE* ME, THAT YOU'D HAVE TO *SEE* IT.

WHAT YOU SEE IS THE *DYING FORM* OF *DOCTOR WILCOX*. BECAUSE HIS HOST-BODY WAS A CLONE OF *LUTHER MANNING*--YOUR BODY BEFORE YOU BECAME DEATHLOK--HIS *MIND TRANSFERENCE* WAS *TEMPORARY*.

YOU DON'T NEED TO *SPELL IT OUT*, LADY. WHEN WILCOX DISCOVERED HE WAS *DYING OF RADIATION POISONING*--

--*MY* PEOPLE PERFORMED AN OPERATION WHICH *SAVED* HIM. BUT AFTER SEVERAL *MONTHS*, THE INEVITABLE REJECTION OF THE DOCTOR'S *BRAIN PATTERNS* HAS BEGUN.

THEN, WHAT YOU'RE SAYING IS-- THERE'S *NO WAY* TO *CURE* ME.

ON THE *CONTRARY*, YOU SEE, THIS *TAPE CONSOLE*--

--IS WHERE HIS *MIND* IS GOING--ONTO A *SPECIAL* TAPE CARTRIDGE TO BE STORED IN OUR *MIND BANKS*.

WE EVEN HAVE A *BLANK* ON WHICH THE *PRESIDENT* IS STORED--

THE PRES--! *DEAD?* I--I DON'T *BELIEVE* YOU.

SEE FOR YOURSELF.

TACTILE ANALYSIS CORROBORATES SUBJECT'S STATEMENT . . .

OKAY. OKAY. I GET THE IDEA.

PLEASE *BELIEVE* ME, DEATHLOK, WHEN I *TELL* YOU--

--THAT *ALL* WE NEED DO IS *DECODE YOUR* BRAIN PATTERNS--

--*MATCH* THEM WITH THE CLONE'S--

--AND WE CAN *CURE* YOU.

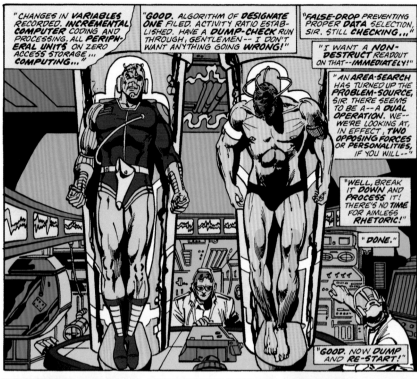

"CHANGES IN *VARIABLES* RECORDED. *INCREMENTAL* *COMPUTER* CODING AND PROCESSING. ALL *PERIPH-ERAL UNITS* ON ZERO ACCESS STORAGE... *COMPUTING...*"

"*GOOD.* ALGORITHM OF *DESIGNATE ONE* FILED. ACTIVITY RATIO ESTAB-LISHED. HAVE A *DUMP-CHECK* RUN THROUGH, GENTLEMEN -- I DON'T WANT ANYTHING GOING *WRONG!*"

"*FALSE-DROP* PREVENTING PROPER *DATA* SELECTION, SIR. STILL *CHECKING...*"

"I WANT A *NON-DESTRUCT* READOUT ON THAT--*IMMEDIATELY!*"

"AN *AREA-SEARCH* HAS TURNED UP THE *PROBLEM-SOURCE,* SIR. THERE SEEMS TO BE A--A *DUAL OPERATION.* WE-- WE'RE LOOKING AT, IN EFFECT, *TWO OPPOSING FORCES* OR *PERSONALITIES,* IF YOU WILL--"

"*WELL,* BREAK IT *DOWN* AND *PROCESS* IT! THERE'S NO *TIME* FOR AIMLESS *RHETORIC!*"

"*DONE.*"

"*GOOD.* NOW DUMP AND RE-*START!*"

"*AFFIRMATIVE.* ATTENDED TIME: 39 SECONDS."

"SIR-- WE SEEM TO BE GETTING AN *ADDITIONAL FUNCTION* READOUT PRO-GRAMMED ON A *BISTABLE CIRCUIT. PROGRAMMING COMPLETE.* IT LOOKS LIKE A *ROGER...*"

IF THIS *WORKS,* LUTHER MANNING WILL BECOME *HIMSELF* AGAIN--NO LONGER A *MONSTER!*

AND *WE* WILL BE LOSING PERHAPS ONE OF THE *BEST OPERATIVES* THE *AGENCY* HAS *EVER HAD.*

I THINK I'D RATHER HAVE THE *MAN* BACK-- --*WHATEVER* THE *PRICE!*

THAT *IS* WHAT WE'RE *FIGHTING* FOR, ISN'T IT, TOM?

THE RIGHT FOR US *ALL...TO BE HUMAN* AGAIN!

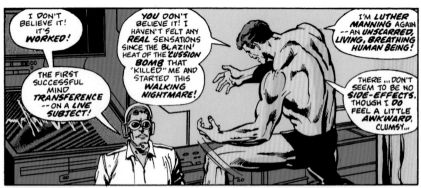

I DON'T BELIEVE IT! IT'S *WORKED!*

THE FIRST SUCCESSFUL MIND *TRANSFERENCE* --ON A *LIVE* SUBJECT!

YOU DON'T BELIEVE IT! I HAVEN'T FELT ANY *REAL* SENSATIONS SINCE THE BLAZIN' HEAT OF THE *'LUSSION BOMB* THAT "KILLED" ME AND STARTED THIS *WALKING NIGHTMARE!*

I'M *LUTHER MANNING* AGAIN --AN *UNSCARRED, LIVING, BREATHING HUMAN BEING!*

THERE ...DON'T SEEM TO BE NO *SIDE-EFFECTS.* THOUGH I *DO* FEEL A LITTLE *AWKWARD,* CLUMSY...

--AND THAT-- *THING* THAT WAS ME-- *DEATHLOK,* IS IT--?

--*DEAD?* HOW CAN A MASS OF COMPUTER CIRCUITS AND *UNLIVING FLESH*--DIE??!

MY GOD! THE *CYBORG*--

--IT'S *STILL* ALIVE!

YOU BET YOUR *BRASS BUTTONS!* IT TOOK MORE'N RYKER TO GET RIDDA ME--

--AN' IT'LL TAKE *MORE* THAN *YOU!*

IT'S *IMPOSSIBLE!* THAT'S ME TALKING ... *MY* VOICE

HOW?! HOW CAN WE *BOTH* EXIST?

HELLINGER TERMINAL EYE READ-OUT: DOOMSDAY MECH APPROACHING FORT DIX...

NEURON-FORCE READY TO BE COME FULLY IMPLEMENTED...

TARGET SELECT: DEATHLOK CYBORG. SEPARA- TION FROM HOST-BODY IMMINENT.

PROJECTION: IN 60 SECONDS...

--THE WORLD WILL GO ON ,LESS *ONE BIONIC MURDER-FREAK!* AND THE *BENEV- OLENT MADNESS* THAT MY *BROTHER* EMPLOYED TO *RUN* THINGS-- WILL BE RENDERED A *MEANINGLESS PRANK.*

NOT SINCE *HITLER...* WILL THE WORLD HAVE KNOWN SUCH *HELL!*

THAT'S ALL FOR NOW, FOLKS! BUT NEVER FEAR, A NEW DEATHLOK THE DEMOLISHER POCKETBOOK WILL BE COMING SOON!

AND SO IT GOES, ALL THROUGH THE LONG NIGHT OF CONSTRUCTIVE TOIL.

IT STINKS, MAN.

IT STINKS.

STINKS.

AND THEN...IT IS FINISHED. THE CULMINATION OF THEIR FERVID COLLABORATION NOW A MATTER OF RECORD.

AH, SO *WHAT* IF WE COULDN'T COME UP WITH ANYTHING GOOD, MAN. NO BIG DEAL.

YEAH. SO *WHAT?*

EVEN AFTER THEY'VE GONE, THE LINGERING ECHO OF THEIR PRIDE HOVERS IN THE NOW HISTORIC OFFICE.

IT WAS A LOUSY IDEA ANYWAY, MAN.

YEAH. IT *STUNK!*

AND AFTER THEY'VE BEEN GONE EVEN LONGER, THE LINGERING ECHO LINGERS... ALBEIT SLIGHTLY SOFTER.

DOOMED FROM THE MOMENT WE STARTED. I MEAN, WHO'D EVER BELIEVE IN A CHARACTER LIKE THAT?

YEAH, AND WITH SUCH A DUMB *NAME.* WE MIGHT AS WELL *FACE* IT--

--DEATHLOK WAS NEVER DESTINED FOR *LIFE.*

DRAWN BY: GEORGE PEREZ & MIKE ESPOSITO

WRITTEN BY: D. M.

AND THE DISTANT SOUND OF TRUMPETS SIGNALS AN END TO THIS MOMENTOUS NIGHT.

R. Buckler '74

Unused Astonishing Tales #26 splash page, which would become issue #27's title page
by Rich Buckler